YOU SHOULD HAVE LISTENED

KAILA WILKEY

ACKNOWLEDGMENTS

To Kaila.
Whose dreams I'll never give up on.
- Winter

FOREWORD

To my readers and supporters, thank you. My life would not be nearly as interesting without you by my side. Remember to chase your dreams with your head held high.

1

MO' PROBLEMS

"NOW, *who's hot, who not? Tell me who rock, who sell out in the stores?*" *Ma$e* was spittin' when he dropped those lines on *B.I.G's* song, *Mo' Money, Mo' Problems.* That was the theme song of my life after wrapping up the reality show and dealing with Demi and her punk ass friend for running off with my fuckin' money.

In case you forgot, I made the very amateur mistake of allowing a couple of bitches that I thought I could trust, to stay in my apartment while I lived through the hell you call entertainment; reality TV. Those dusty bitches were stealing my shit and pocketing the rent money I was sending every month instead of paying the bills. Broke ass bitches were stealing from me and still couldn't afford to boss their lives up for real. On top of that, Demi's little friend stole my brand new bottle of *Issey Miyake*, the sweetest perfume you will ever smell. Guaranteed to make a nigga dick jump. I was hot but it was what it was because I knew I would get mine every time I saw her out.

Honestly, my life was sort of in shambles after all of that. Not just because of the Demi situation. It was a number of things combined. Shit will always look good from the outside looking in because I'm not the type to let anyone see that I'm struggling - but things were bad. Really bad. After the show, I was mentally in the worst space I had ever been in my entire life. Ironically enough, I was making more money than I had ever made in my entire life, too. But, more money, more problems, right?

See, as entertaining as the show must have been for the viewers, it was equally as draining for me. Don't get me wrong, it was an incredible opportunity overall because like I told you before, the show changed my whole life, but I could have very easily done without being villainized. On the other hand, my online store was poppin', I was always booked, my DM's were going up even more than before, and it was looking like I would never have to dance again thanks to the platform that the show had given me.

All of the good that came from my time on the show came at a price. Unfortunately, it was a price that held no monetary value. It cost me my mental health. You know by now that I've always found pride in being able to stay true to who I am no matter what I've been through. So, at the price of compromising my character, the show put me in a position to win, but the fact still remains that it was very fucking ghetto. The truth is that I had no clue that my character and my mental health would be the price I had to pay. I mean, let's really look at the facts. I had never done TV before, so it was fair for me to assume that I would go on the show and just be myself. There was no way in hell for me to even guess that the producers would pin me as the bad guy. Like I told you before, I genuinely believed it was going to be a fucking walk in the park and I was going to be the main attraction. Well, I was right about the part where I was the main attraction, but that doesn't negate the fact that I was unhappy with how things played out.

We've already talked about this, but it still follows me around to this day. When I say the show compromised my character, it did so by painting me out to be a bully. They only labeled me that way because producers convinced me to pick on some skinny, strung out looking bitch because "the show was getting boring". That was my bad for falling into that though. I've never been the type to pick on the little guy. If anything I was the little guy growing up. The only difference between me and the skinny bitch was that I won't play victim, I'll always get my lick back. I'm a firm believer that you can only be bullied if you let a muthafucka bully you. Simple. That's neither here nor there because once the internet decides they know you based off of a few photos or a few scenes from a show, it's almost impossible to convince them otherwise. Let me set the record straight for the last time. What people watched on the show was a direct reflection of what the producers wanted them to see. They created narratives for every girl in that house and then did hella sneaky shit behind the scenes in order to bring those narratives to life. Our hell was your entertainment.

I'm not going to front like I didn't fall into the trap but everything I did was in response to something done to me. The gag was that most times, you were only able to see my reaction–not what I was reacting to. Could I have handled a few situations better? I'm a real ass bitch, so I don't have a problem answering that question honestly: "yes." But the producers had all of us on some bullshit, not just me.

Anyway, after dealing with the whole Demi situation, you'd think I would have learned my lesson, but I didn't and I ended up having a friend of mine move in with me. You already know what types of living situations I've been through in the past from crashing at my aunt's house, being banned from Lily's house, and sleeping on a couch in a meth house basement. All of which were worse than some dumb bitch and her homegirl stealing from me, so I just feel like you should understand why I continued to make the same mistake over and over again. My heart is big and my love is pure. Period. Besides all of that, Destinee was one of my best friends at the time and us living together was a no brainer. Especially since I was still going through the emotions of my break up with Xavier.

When I think back on it all, I never really had time to properly grieve or heal from the break up because I basically went right into the show and then right after that, I went home to the Demi drama. It wasn't until all the smoke cleared that I realized how deep into depression I had fallen. I was left to face my emotions and I'm sure it would have been best for me to do that alone, but that's not how life worked out. Xavier was still messaging me on a regular basis which is right on brand, because you know niggas will always try to spin the block. It probably would have been fine if he wasn't in a whole ass public relationship with that girl Honey that he cheated on me with right before the show.

It broke my heart to read messages from him while he paraded around with another bitch because it was like I was watching the love of my life do things he had never done for me, for a bitch he barely knew, and it sent me even deeper into my depression. It was a hard pill to swallow because it didn't make sense to me how he could do that to me. Why would you continue to message your ex-girlfriend when you already have a new bitch? Men are so damn embarrassing.

Between the backlash I was getting from the show and the love of my life playing mind games with me, I just wanted to disappear. At that point in time, I was somewhere between living my best life and not wanting to do life at all. I was lost, heartbroken, misunderstood by a majority of the people who knew of me, and no matter how many people surrounded me, I just felt painfully alone.

As I struggled through my depression, I continued to run my store, *Frost*, write songs, and plot on how I'd make my next move, the best move. While I was dealing with all that shit, I would still find time to go outside and have fun. I'm using the term fun very loosely because honestly, it only felt fun in the moment. I would go out just to keep my mind off of the things that I was struggling with internally, but when the night ended, it never made me feel any better.

One of those "fun" nights, while I was at the club, I met a football player and we clicked instantly. There wasn't anything spectacular about the way that we met or how our first date went because it was simple: we met and he took me out to dinner shortly after that. Like every other relationship I've been in, things started to move very quickly after our first date. You'd think a football player that stood at about six feet seven inches and weighed close to three hundred pounds would be a fuck boy, but Eric was far from that. Instead, he was the sweetest, most patient man ever; a whole teddy bear. I'm a playa first but a sap directly after that so I really enjoyed having Eric's country bumpkin ass in my life. He was just what I needed at the time; someone who valued and understood me. Well, I mean, I probably needed therapy more than anything, but having a man that spoiled me was doing a damn good job at pulling me out of my depression.

Regardless of how much I liked Eric, I knew better than to fall too deep because whether he was a teddy bear or not, I knew then like I know now that a nigga gone always be a nigga. I had experienced enough heartbreak to know that no matter how good a man treated me, he had the potential to hurt me worse if I allowed him to and I didn't have the mental capacity to play that bullshit ass game with Eric. I wasn't willing to run the risk of yet another heartbreak. And not-so-lucky for me, I had so much shit going on mentally and emotionally that initially, it was fairly easy for me to keep him at a distance. I had convinced both my mind and my heart that we were there for a good time, not a long time.

Eric began to spoil me very early into our relationship and even though I was making my own money and could afford to buy whatever I wanted, I liked spending his money instead because why the fuck wouldn't I? We ate at restaurants that I had never eaten at before and we slept in hotels and visited spas that I could only dream to be real. Eric opened my mind up to new feelings and experiences. Beyond all of the material things, he really gave me the affection that I needed, in a time where I was so defeated by what felt like the entire world. That shit just felt good across the board and somehow, out of nowhere, I fucked around and caught real feelings for him. It didn't dawn on me until he asked me to move in with him that within just three months of meeting each other, dating and becoming best friends, I had done more than just 'catch feelings'. I was damn near in love.

Besides the fact that it was a beautiful house in Calabasas, I was spending a majority of my time with him anyway so living together made sense. So much for being there for a good time and not a long time because once I moved in, there wasn't anything you could tell me to convince me that I would leave him or that he would leave me. Now, that doesn't mean that I abandoned my apartment because I knew the fuck better.

Listen, girl, if you don't learn anything else from me, I genuinely want you to learn this: ALWAYS HAVE YOUR OWN! I can't stress that enough. It doesn't matter how much money these men have, how many gifts they buy you or how much they love you, it's imperative that you build your own fortune and maintain your own stability and individuality outside of that relationship--because nobody can ever 'send you back to the streets' if you own the block. And yes, ownership is important, but if you're not in a position to do that just yet, be sure to always put something away so that you always land on your feet if or when a man starts to act up.

With that being said, moving in with Eric was an easy decision because I was comfortable financially and knew that he could only elevate my life. After coming out of my relationship with Xavier, watching him move on to a relationship with Honey, and feeling like my character had been stripped down because of the show, being with Eric made me feel like I was 'enough'. His attentiveness and the way he was so enamored with me boosted my confidence and even though no one could tell from looking on the outside--on the inside, I really needed that. And I can't front, even though Destinee was living with me, I still felt alone in some sense so the idea of moving in with Eric, sort of alleviated that feeling of loneliness.

Look, back then, I was struggling to find my way out of a very dark space emotionally and I know now that filling those voids or hiding my pain by completely avoiding it wasn't the proper way to handle things but it's what worked for me at the time. Today, I know and understand the importance of unpacking the pain so that I can heal it properly. I've given my therapist a whole lot of money to help me understand that so I have no problem keeping it real with you whenever I speak on a situation.

It seems like as soon as I moved into Eric's house, he multiplied the way he spoiled me ten times. I'm talking about waking up to stacks of money on the bed, dozens and dozens of roses every week, all types of shit. My friends were always at the house with me too, so he would give me money so that we could all go shopping and have spa days. We would go to expensive ass restaurants for lunch and even go to the strip club to cash bitches out and we did all of that on Eric's dime. When my girls weren't there, he and I would just be laid up enjoying one another's company. Occasionally, he would go out of town on business trips or down south to spend time with his daughter and I would just be at home taking bubble baths and walking around the house in a plush ass robe, enjoying the fruits of my labor as a girlfriend. Being a girlfriend was damn near my job at the time and being spoiled was my compensation. Of course, *Frost* was bringing in a steady cash flow, but I was able to save all of the profits because Eric was taking care of me so well.

I'm not sure if I was falling in love with Eric or the lifestyle he provided for me but either way, it was all short lived. About three months into my live-in girlfriend position, Eric was out of town on business again and I was doing what spoiled girlfriends do: taking a bubble bath. I was looking like *Rev Run* – Revina Run, if you will, while minding everybody else's business on social media, casually scrolling through the comments of one of the most popular entertainment blogs. Somehow, I made my way to Eric's comments and thought that I would be scrolling through just to see what thirsty bitches that could never have him had to say, only to scroll across a comment that implied he was cheating on me. It was a simple comment that said, *can't wait to see you again*, with a pink heart emoji and some heart eyes. My heart skipped a beat and my cheeks got warm. I leaned over the bathtub so that my phone was no longer hovering over the water in order to eliminate the risk of dropping it in the middle of an important investigation.

My first thought to myself was, *see, you should've listened*. I was angry. I was angry with Eric for being like every other man but I was angry with myself for opening my heart up to yet another disappointing man. There were so many pieces of me that I had shared with him over the months that we had been together. There were so many layers of my protective walls that I had taken down for him, just for him to betray me. I knew better. I knew better than to open up to that man about what I had gone through. I also knew better than to allow myself to care about him because I knew that it wouldn't last long. Unfortunately, knowing better didn't force me to do better.

Some part of me wanted to believe that the comment I read was cap. I wanted to believe that maybe I had misunderstood the context of the message because Eric was different from the rest and wouldn't do me like that. It didn't matter that in the past, he had shown me photos and told me names of every woman that used to mean something to him because I was reaching for the slight possibility that maybe he had accidentally left this one out. I knew the truth though. I felt it in my stomach the way us women always do. As I leaned over the side of the bathtub with my phone in my hands, I took a deep breath and began to scroll through the woman's page. It didn't take long for me to scroll across a photo of her in his bathroom, the same one I was taking a bath in. The photo was posted six months prior to the date, but her comment on his post had only been made two weeks prior to the day I saw it.

I laughed sarcastically as I shook my head in disbelief. "This has to be a fucking joke." I said out loud, swallowing down the lump in my throat.

I've never been one to put my hands on a man and I definitely wasn't going to start with Eric. Especially after I had damn near died at the hands of Cinco after he beat me and left me for dead, but I remember wishing that I could have beat Eric's ass. He knew how much betrayal and heartbreak I had experienced and then he turned around and did the same bullshit. I couldn't believe I allowed myself to catch feelings for him, but I wasn't about to sit in that bathtub and sulk in my sorrows. I took a moment to shed a few tears and stomach the pain of betrayal before I drained the water and gathered my thoughts.

Almost instantly, I went from sad and hurt to remembering that playa's fuck up too. And the moment that I was able to remind myself who the fuck I was, I was able to remove any cap ass emotions I thought I felt so that I could get my lick back. Eric really fucking tried me by cheating in the first place, but he let me find out on the internet and that's where he had me fucked up.

There was no way in hell that I was going to wait for Eric to get back from his business trip before I decided to let him know that he had made a huge mistake.

The phone barely rang before he answered, "Hey, babe." Eric said.

"Don't fuckin' 'hey, babe' me nigga! You got me fucked up. Why the fuck is some bitch in your comments talking about she can't wait to see you? Do you know who I am? You're a fuck boy just like the rest of these cap ass muthafuckas!" I yelled into the phone.

"Babe. No." Eric took a deep breath. "Babe, that's not what you think it is, ok? Look, we'll talk when I get home. I'll book the first flight back. I promise it's..."

I didn't let him finish. "Keep your sorry ass promises. I don't care when you come back. I won't be here. I'm done. You're weak as fuck for this." I said, trying to fight back tears.

To be honest, I'm not even sure if I was really as heartbroken or angry as I was coming off to be. Did I like Eric, yes. Besides cheating, he was really good to me. I'm not going to act like being a professional girlfriend, being spoiled, spoiling my friends, and saving hella money for a few months wasn't lit as fuck, because it was. I think more than anything, it was the betrayal and the complete disregard of my past that really fucked me up. What Eric had done to me wasn't any worse than what any man from the past had done, so in some disgusting way, I was used to it; maybe even immune to it. I will say that it birthed something new inside of me, though. It activated a new level of savageness within me.

After hanging up on Eric, I threw on some sweats, had a glass of wine and decided to go back home. For whatever reason, when I left, I didn't take any of my stuff with me, but I left my copy of the house key on the middle of the bed so that I could be sure Eric would see it when he got home. I wanted him to know that I was dead ass serious about leaving him.

By the time I made it to my apartment, I had about twenty text messages from Eric and they were all him apologizing like the sorry ass nigga that he was. That wasn't enough for me though. I wanted Eric to feel my wrath. I wanted him to know that just because I had experienced so much heartache behind men, it didn't mean that I needed one. Getting spoiled is all fun and games until it doesn't include respect. I don't give a fuck who you are, who you play for, who you're signed to, how much money you have or any of that other shit; if you disrespect me, it's up. Eric disrespected me so you know I had to step.

The next morning, Eric left four voicemails and seven more text messages.

The first message said, "Kay. Call me back." He sounded defeated. His voice was low and raspy.

The second message said, "Babe, I booked you a flight. I'm sorry. Call me back." He was still defeated but there was a little more determination in his voice.

Hearing the second message pissed me off so much that I didn't even bother listening to the other two. The night before, he told me that he was going to book the first flight available so that he could come home and we could talk. But instead, he leaves a voicemail telling me that he booked a flight for me. He must have been out of his fucking mind if he really thought I was about to hop on a fucking flight to go see his cheating ass. It pissed me off even more just thinking about the audacity it took to go from 'I'll come home' to 'you're coming here'. He didn't even fucking ask me if I wanted to drop what I was doing to hop on a flight. Granted, I could have gone if I wanted to but I don't jump just because a man says so.

His text messages were screenshots of the flight itinerary and more apologies. Quite frankly, I didn't want any of it and I definitely wasn't in the mood to entertain it. He deserved to be in the dark about how I felt, the same way he left me in the dark about whatever the fuck him and that hoe had going on. I literally went on with the rest of my day as if I had never read or listened to any of Eric's messages. I treated myself to a massage, a beautiful solo lunch date on a rooftop, and then handled a few things that needed to be done for *Frost*. One thing about it, a man will never stop my hustle or prevent me from spoiling my damn self. If anything, every time a man fucks up, I make more money and get even finer.

After a full day of ignoring Eric, spending money and handling business, four of my homegirls pulled up on Destinee and I at my place so that I could get them caught up on everything that had transpired. After a few drinks, I decided that I wanted to go to Eric's house to pick up all of my shit before he got back in town. I had hella clothes and all types of other shit at his house and since I was done with him, I wanted all of it. It didn't matter to me that he had paid for every thing that belonged to me in his house because once you give me a gift, it's mine. What was he going to do with it? Give it to the next bitch? Please. *Play "Ring the Alarm" by Beyoncè.*

Between the liquor and all the shit me and my girls had talked about, I decided that not only was I going to go pick up my shit, I was going to make Eric pay for the inconvenience he had caused me. The little social media bitch wasn't even cuter than me, she clearly didn't have more money than me, and I was willing to bet a hundred bands that she didn't have any type of substance. She was just another groupie that was excited to be seen by a man of Eric's caliber. Unfortunately, Eric was just another man excited to be seen by yet another groupie. They were both idiots and they both deserved to have their asses beat.

I know you're probably thinking like *this crazy bitch* and you're right. The thing is that I didn't care then and I don't care right now – I stand ten toes down on every decision I make in life. It'll either make me some money or create some damn good memories and either way, I'm going to do whatever I want to do, every time. Anyway, my girls and I all hopped in the car and drove straight to Eric's house. There wasn't much of a plan on what we would do when we got there other than I wanted all of my stuff and somehow, he needed to pay for what he had done.

When we finally made it to his house, we low key had to break in because remember, I had left my key on the bed when I initially left the house and the front door locked on its own. Breaking in wasn't even a challenge though because I just crawled through the doggie door and then deactivated the alarm system. Mind you, we had been drinking, so we were all laughing hysterically at the fact that my ass was on all fours crawling through a doggie door. We were loud and obnoxious as if we weren't running the risk of being caught and going to jail.

Obviously I knew we weren't really going to get caught, but the first thing we did once I opened the door was run upstairs to pack up all of my stuff. We put everything into a couple of *Louis Vuitton* duffle bags that were in Eric's closet and rushed the bags to my car as quickly as we could. Getting through the doggie door took a little longer than we expected and I hadn't spoken to Eric all day so there was no real way to know whether or not he would be pulling up while we were there and the last thing I wanted to do was see him. From start to finish, it took us about thirty minutes to break in, grab my shit, and load the *Audi*. Once we were done, we all stood around my car looking at one another and then we bursted into laughter.

"Nah, I think we have more time." I said to my homegirls.

Destinee stopped laughing and said, "Well, shit, I saw hella liquor in there and you said he has to pay for the inconvenience so let's get it back in bottles!"

We all laughed again.

I started to walk toward the house again and said, "Let's really piss him off!"

The girls yelled in excitement like we were some tiny little war soldiers.

Keep in mind, I didn't have a real plan on what we would do to piss Eric off, we were just going to wing it. When we got back inside of his house, we headed straight for the kitchen and took all of his good liquor, food and snacks and packed them into my car, too. It became more fun after that because for whatever reason, I wasn't satisfied yet with what we had already done and I wanted to be even more petty. I wanted him to get home from his trip and feel like he didn't have control over the situation. I wanted him to feel as inconvenienced as he made me feel. And I wanted to make sure that he felt my absence in as many ways as possible; he needed to think about missing me everyday.

"Let's go get his shoes." I said.

We all ran upstairs, laughing like children. I don't even remember how I came up with this idea, but we started taking all of the left shoes from his shoe closet and putting them into my car as well. I'm not going to lie, as childish as it was, it felt good. I was starting to feel some form of liberation and I loved it. By the end of my revenge rampage, me and my girls had walked out of Eric's house with his left shoes, my clothes, food, liquor, remote controls, and anything else I could find that I knew would piss him off when he realized it was gone. We even emptied out his drawers and tried our best to rip his underwear up. We weren't strong enough but we stretched them out enough to where he would definitely have to buy all new pairs.

We had finally done all the damage we were going to do and realized that since there were so many of us and we piled so much stuff into my car, there wasn't enough room for all of us. That was when I decided that we also needed to take a few of his cars just to make sure we all got home safely. We took a *Rolls Royce*, *Porsche* truck, and an *Escalade* back to my house. Of course the logical thing to do would have been to put some of the stuff that didn't actually belong to me, back into the house so that there would be enough room in my truck for each of us. But we weren't moving in logic that night; it was just immaturity and vibes. If you ain't never got your lick back by being petty and immature, you haven't lived.

Side note: shout out to my girls for being down ass bitches. Thinking back to that night always cracks me up because what type of shit was that? Why would I do that? Why didn't they think twice about helping me? We all need friends like them.

Anyways back to the story, you play stupid games, you win stupid prizes and we made sure Eric was a champion. My girls and I spent the rest of the night celebrating his big win by drinking his liquor, eating his food, taking pictures in his cars, and hanging all of my clothes up. By the time we were done, we were able to find all of the social media handles of the little bitch that he cheated on me with. In general, I know that you're supposed to be mad at your nigga for cheating on you and not the bitch he cheated with, but she knew we were in a relationship because he and I posted each other publicly. So since she made the decision to fuck with my man knowingly I felt she deserved a prize too. The plan was to keep tabs on her until she posted a location where I could pull up. Whenever a groupie bitch is out somewhere that is considered to be a hotspot, they can't wait to post about it, so I knew it wouldn't be long before she led me right to her.

In the meantime, Eric had gotten home two days after we had broken into his house and he wasn't as upset as I thought he'd be, which actually took a lot of the fun out of the whole thing. Like, sir, you don't have any left shoes and three of your cars are gone, why the hell aren't you upset? It made no sense to me, but what made even less sense was that he still wanted to be with me. He knew that he was dead ass wrong for what he had done and made sure he kept reiterating that in every text message he sent. Maybe in his mind, what I had done was a small price for him to pay for his actions. I don't know. Whatever the case, he didn't give a shit that I had broken into his house and took his stuff.

A week had gone by and he never even asked me to return his clothing or his cars and to make things even more confusing, he was damn near begging me to move down south with him. He wanted to do the whole family thing out there with me and his daughter. It never ceases to amaze me that men always want to become family men after they fuck up. I'm sorry, but at twenty-three years old and finally having all of my own shit, what the hell did I look like being a whole stepmom? Let's not forget that years before that, I played that role when I was with Cinco, and it clearly didn't work out so well. Eric knew all of that shit. I may not have shared how deeply painful those things were for me, with him, but he definitely knew that I had gone through some shit. So why, in anyone's right mind, would they think I would want to become a stepmom or play the wife role so soon? Besides that, did Eric really think I was going to give up my dream of becoming a music artist just to move to butt fuck Egypt to live up under a man who cheated on me? That wasn't even an option I was willing to entertain but I've never been blind to opportunity. If Eric still wanted me after I burglarized his house and stole his cars, I felt like I could have gotten whatever I wanted from him. So, after about two weeks of making him beg me to come home, I ultimately decided to take him back and 'work on our relationship'.

You're probably thinking that me staying with him goes against any and everything I ever say about dealing with a cheating man or any man that doesn't value you the way he should. But I know just like you know that sometimes, life doesn't work that way. Outside of his infidelity, Eric spoiled the fuck out of me, which was cool but you have to remember that I was not in a great space mentally and emotionally before I met him. When I met Eric, I was dying on the inside and he was the person that helped me keep my mind off of everything I had dealt with and was still dealing with when it came to Xavier, as well as the public scrutiny I was receiving from my time on the show.

Now, I can look back and understand that this was an unhealthy pattern because when I was with Xavier, he was the person that helped me keep my mind off of all of the emotional and physical abuse I had dealt with when I was with Cinco. Cinco helped me keep my mind off of Jail Bae, who if you remember, had done me dirty while he was in jail by having a whole other underaged girlfriend besides me. It's as clear as a VVS diamond that I was packing my pain away instead of dealing with it, but I don't think I would have survived any other way. At the end of the day, you have to do what's best for you, because everybody else is doing what's best for them.

Alright, back to what I was saying, I'm sure I've told you

before that I hold grudges until I feel as though you've paid for what you've done to me. If I didn't tell you, well, now you know. With that being said, two months had passed since I had found out about Eric cheating and we were doing fine. Not fine like I had moved down south and started being a stepmom fine, but no arguing, I moved back into the Calabasas spot, fine. Regardless, I was still keeping tabs on the girl he cheated with because for one, I needed to make sure he wasn't still cheating with her and two, I owed her an ass whooping. And let me just say that I am so happy that I've been able to grow out of this bullshit. Girl, if you have to keep tabs on another bitch to make sure your man isn't fucking with her, free yourself from the shackles of stress and stupidity. Ain't no dick that good.

So, one night, after a dinner date with Eric, he dropped me off at home and went to play poker with a few of his boys. Being the rich, stay-at-home girlfriend that I was, I decided to end my night with a bubble bath and a glass of champagne. While my bath water ran, I decided to check the bitches socials just to make sure he wasn't actually spending time with her instead of the boys like he said he would be doing. Honestly, I knew he wasn't fucking with her anymore but I still had to check. I didn't expect to see anything entertaining on any of her pages because she was actually a very boring bitch, but I was just looking for the smallest clue that she was with him. We all know that if she was, there would have been a shoe, an ear lobe, a car selfie, a fucking thread from his jeans–anything she could capture, in her post.

By the way, for that entire two months, I still had his cars and left shoes. For the life of me, I still don't understand why that man didn't press charges, leave me alone, or try to intimidate me into giving them back but he didn't. Instead, he just kept begging me to return them and I just kept telling him that he needed to prove that he deserved them. I was driving those cars around like they were mine, my girls and I were pulling up to the clubs in a different car every weekend. It was a time to be alive honestly.

Anyway, the little thirsty bitch he cheated on me with posted that she was at *Nobu* and regardless of the fact that Eric and I were doing fine, I saw that as the perfect opportunity to pull up and give her the prize that she earned when she chose to disrespect me. I wasn't really concerned about whether or not Eric would be upset with me for beating her ass or not. He could have left me for all I cared, I was just in a place where I was tired of bitches thinking that I was one to be played with. On top of that she was throwing a lot of little subliminals that I let slide way too many times.

When I saw her post, I immediately called Destinee.

"We got a location, bitch. Get dressed!" I said as I quickly turned off my bath water.

Confused, Destinee was like, " A location on who, bitch?"

Before I could reply, it dawned on her. "Oh! Yes! Pull the fuck up! Come get me!" Destinee said.

It took me no time at all to throw on some sweats and scoop Destinee up. I don't know how we pulled this off, but we arrived at *Nobu* just in time. The little bitch and her girls were waiting in the valet area.

When I hopped out of my car and called her name, she began to laugh.

"I don't even know you!" She said as I approached her.

Right before I lit her face up I said, " You knew me when you were sitting on my man's dick!!"

After that, I snatched her by the hair and dragged her into the street. This bitch was a lot bigger in person so I would have assumed she could fight but she just let me beat her ass and was screaming for help. When the Valet workers finally pulled me off of her, her face was bloody and she was screaming about how I had broken her nose. I didn't actually break her nose by the way, I just don't think she had ever gotten her ass beat before and was in shock. I almost felt bad for the bitch until I remembered all the subs she was making about me online. All that talk gets really expensive when you have to throw hands to pay for it.

That night, I dropped Destinee off at the house and went back to Eric's house and stormed through the bedroom door to tell him what I had done. It was like I had gotten angry about it all over again. All of my emotions had resurfaced and were overwhelming me. As I was yelling at him, I was crying and telling him how angry I was at him for hurting and embarrassing me. It was a surreal moment because I was yelling at Eric, but it reminded me of the night I stormed into the bedroom to press Cinco about fucking a bitch from the club and the night I got fired from my job and walked in on Xavier laid up with with somebody else. It was a feeling that was all too familiar for me. One that I hadn't healed from the first or second time and obviously wasn't even close to healing from the third time.

Eric didn't care that I had beat her up, he didn't care that I was yelling at him or calling him out of his name. All he cared about was making me feel better in that moment and trying to convince me that I was the only one he wanted to be with for the rest of his life. I mean, what else was he supposed to do? He moved slowly from the bed where he was sitting and walked over to me in the doorway of the bedroom. He wrapped his arms around me and squeezed my body against his as if his hug could mold all my broken pieces back together.

"Let's start over, baby. We can start over in Alabama." He kept saying as he hugged me.

Without embracing his body the way he did mine, I just stood there. I didn't have any more words. I didn't truly understand why I had been so emotional, I just knew that I was tired of being hurt and played with. For the rest of the night, we just sat on the bed as the sound of music drowned out the silence. It was like he knew that there was nothing he could say to me but he also knew that I wasn't going to leave – the same way I knew that I wasn't going to leave.

I knew that I didn't want to move to Alabama — hell, I knew that I didn't want to be with him at all anymore, but I also knew that I didn't want to be alone. I'm not going to lie, I was genuinely hurt, but I was used to that shit, so some part of me just didn't care. At that point it was like, if he wanted me to stay, he was going to have to pay. Now, there was no way I was going to completely move to Alabama, but by the end of the night, I came up with a few terms and conditions under which I would be willing to compromise.

The first thing I demanded was a house in LA. My own house, in my name. It sounds far-fetched, but it wasn't. Eric had the bag to make it happen. Basically, I told him that it was the least he could do after hurting me and embarrassing me the way he did. Truth be told, it had nothing to do with what he had done, I just wanted to see if he was going to get me the house or not. Toxic, I know, but I was already checked out of the relationship emotionally and I wasn't ready to be a stepmom, so I didn't feel like I had anything to lose by asking for the house. At first, I was thinking that I should have packaged it in a way that made him feel like it made the most sense for us to have homes in both states but I didn't have it in me to kiss his ass when he should have been kissing mine.

See, I should've listened to that first thought, because it probably would have worked out in my favor but I didn't and Eric wasn't fucking with it. He felt as though I was only with him for the money and he was hurt that I wasn't interested in being a stepmother to his daughter. There was really no room for me to argue with him on either of those things.

Even though I had never been with a man for his money, I'm not going to stop a man from spending his money on me. Eric and I met at a time where emotionally, I was probably at my lowest, but financially, I was definitely at my highest. I didn't start fucking with him because of his money – it was just a perk. But let's be honest, if every man I have ever dealt with had money, and each one had more than the last, what the fuck do I look like dealing with a man who doesn't have a bag? The math won't math any other way. So, yes, his money was one of the things that qualified him to fuck with me, but please believe that I didn't need him for it.

In a way, I was offended that he was basically trying to call me a gold digger but I didn't care enough to fight it because I knew that it wasn't a fact. Needless to say, by the end of the night, he arranged for his cars to be picked up from my place, apologized for hurting me, and helped me load all of my belongings into my car before I left. I think that it was the most mature thing we had done in that relationship because I stated my demands, he wasn't willing to meet them, and we both gracefully walked away from the table. The relationship was fun and beneficial while it lasted and not that it matters, but that's more than a lot of bitches can say about their relationships.

2

BETRAYAL

ABOUT A MONTH HAD PASSED after my break up with Eric and I was mostly using that time to focus on my business. If I'm being honest, I was also deliberately avoiding any real healing. Money was good, my living situation was solid, and I had a good core group of friends – but internally, I was a shit show. My thoughts were always all over the place because there was a void within me that I couldn't figure out how to fill. Some nights I would lay in bed and think about how much I had endured in life in order to be in the position I was in, yet somehow, I was still struggling mentally and emotionally. My negative thoughts were always met with thoughts of confusion because although I had come from a life of crashing on couches, dancing at strip clubs, and some-times having no money at all, I overcame each of those obstacles and many more by believing in and staying true to myself. As a result of this, I knew that I didn't really *need* anyone because everything I needed was inside of me. It was still hard to shake that feeling of emptiness.

Comparing the life that I came from to the life I had,

should have been enough to make me the happiest person in the world, but it wasn't. Don't get me wrong, I was grateful for how far I had come. I was also grateful that the success I had achieved could only be attributed to my own perseverance and not because of a handout from anyone. After all I had been through, I never wanted anybody to be able to take credit for my come up – especially not a man. I'll be damned if a man ever tried to say he made me.

Anyway, the feeling of lack that I carried had nothing to do with money like it did for so many years in the past, and it obviously had nothing to do with lack of gratitude or growth either. I had grown so much from my experience on the show alone, but in general, I had grown a lot as a woman as well. The issue was that not knowing where the lack stemmed from made it feel damn near impossible to fill that void. It didn't make any sense to me but I guess I just felt alone, misunderstood, undervalued and extremely unappreciated. Today, looking back at where I was in life, it makes complete sense that I would have felt that way because up until that point in my life, not one man valued or respected me the way he should have and I had been crossed by more fake friends than I'd like to admit.

One night as I sat in the middle of my bed trying to write poems in my notebook, my thoughts were interrupted by the idea of just packing all of my shit and moving out of LA. With everything I had experienced between the show, Xavier, Eric, and my own mental chaos, I knew that I needed a change. I needed a fresh start so that I could shift the negative energy that filled my mind, body, and spirit. At the time, my thoughts were becoming so dark that they scared me. Each day that passed was another day that I wasn't sure whether or not I was worthy of life. The crazy part is that if you would have seen me back then, you would have never guessed that I was suffering so many battles in silence. The silence was loud for me though and I knew that it was becoming too loud when it prevented me from doing something I absolutely loved; writing. The only other thing that kept me from drowning was Orien, my cat.

There I was, sitting in the middle of a bed that I paid for, inside of an apartment that was all mine, trying to write poems in my notebook but the only thing I could do was cry. Tears slowly rolled down my cheek and landed on the paper, smearing the ink. There was no specific reason that caused me to cry but there was also no specific reason not to cry. I knew that Destinee was sitting in the living room and I didn't want her to hear me so I did my best to cry silently. I kept telling myself that I had nothing to cry about and tried to coach myself into being strong but it was pointless because the tears continued to roll down my cheeks. All of the pain that I constantly suppressed year after year, heartbreak after heartbreak, was finally catching up to me.

After about five minutes of crying I decided it was enough. I was in a battle with my own brain, actively fighting off depression but I didn't know that yet. I knew there had to be a solution to the emptiness I was feeling — one that didn't require a long emotional healing journey. I wiped my tears, went to my bathroom and stared in the mirror. *Remember who the fuck you are.* I told myself out loud. It seemed as if I was forgetting, or maybe just confused. When the outside world is telling you who you are daily, you might start to forget too. At that moment I decided I needed to get out of Los Angeles and move to somewhere completely new. I don't know why I assumed this was the answer to all my problems but at the time it seemed to make so much sense. I briefly thought of a couple different states and within sixty seconds flat I decided I was moving to Atlanta, Georgia.

"You ready to move to Atlanta, son?" I said as I picked Orien up and kissed his nose.

My mind was made up, I didn't have any real plan in place but there wasn't anything anyone could tell me to convince me that I wouldn't get to Atlanta and be just as successful as I had already been in LA. The way I saw it was that I was built for shit like that. I was built for turning absolutely nothing into something and I was determined to make sure that moving across the country was no different.

Now, even though I knew that Destinee would move without question, I wanted to make sure that I presented the idea to her properly because I was going to be asking her to uproot her entire life just so that I wouldn't feel alone. Granted, she was living with me so there wasn't really going to be much of a difference for her, but it was still a big commitment to move across America and I wanted to respect the fact that she obviously had a right to choose.

I spent the rest of my night looking at apartment complexes online so that I could call a few of them the next morning and check their leasing availability. In order to make the process as smooth as I possibly could, I also hit up the only person I knew out there; my homegirl Amber. She and I had met through mutual friends a few years before and even though we weren't super close, we were close enough for me to tell her that I would be moving to Atlanta. I was surprised but grateful when she offered to check out the available units in the building that she lived in. To be honest, her offering to help me out like that was a sign to me. A sign that I was making the right decision. I decided that I would get all the details together so that when I presented the idea to Destinee I had the answers to every question she might have. I looked up moving fees, apartment price averages, how much it would cost to ship our cars out there. I was serious about this move.

Anyway, by the time I was done planning a new life for Destinee, Orien and I, I had also hit Eric up to tell him that I'd be moving. It was the first time we had spoken since our breakup but it was a good conversation. He seemed to be doing well and he was really happy that I was doing something as wild as moving across the country for a fresh start. As a matter of fact, he was so happy for me that he said he'd buy furniture for the new place once I found it. That on top of planning the rest of my move really lifted my spirits. I really believed that I was about to begin living the life I deserved. I was motivated to get back to my music, grow my business even more, and completely forget about my past. It felt good to just feel good again.

The next morning, before I even made one single phone call, I made my way to the living room because I knew that Destinee had fallen asleep on the couch like she always did.

"Good morning, hoe. We're moving to Atlanta." I said as I playfully jumped on top of her body.

Destinee barely opened her eyes. "We're moving where? What?" She said as she attempted to push me off of her.

With the amount of happiness I felt that morning, you would have never guessed I had been in my room crying my eyes out the night before.

"Atlanta. We're moving to Atlanta." I said directly into her ear. "Me, you, and Orien are getting up out of here!"

I finally hopped off of Destinee and onto the couch. As she attempted to gather herself and make sense of what I had just said to her, I sat there with a huge smile on my face as if I had just given her the best news she ever received.

"Kay, what are you talking about?" Destinee said as she stretched through loud laughter.

"Look." I showed her a screenshot of an apartment complex. "This one is the building Amber lives in. She's going to go see their available unit today and tell me what it looks like."

By that time, Destinee knew that I wasn't joking.

"Kaila, why are we moving to Atlanta? What the hell?" Destinee was genuinely confused.

There was no way I was going to tell her that we were moving because I was lonely, depressed, and felt like I wasn't good enough.

Instead, I said, "Destinee, there's so much opportunity for us out there. You can help me run *Frost*, I can get way more help with my music out there, it's a great place for us to start fresh and you know Atlanta is lit." I pulled that answer right out of my ass.

She was shocked but you could tell that what I said made complete sense to her. "Ok, so when are you trying to move?" She said slowly.

I shifted my body into a more comfortable position on the couch and said, "If you're down, and the apartment in Amber's building is cute, I'll tell this apartment manager that I'm moving out in two weeks." I stared at her, hoping she wouldn't throw out any objections.

"Bitch, you're crazy." Destinee said as she placed her face into the palms of her hands. She was quiet for a second and then said, "Alright, fuck it. Let's move to Atlanta." She looked at me and shrugged her shoulders.

That's one thing I always loved about Destinee, she was down for the bullshit just as much as I was. I knew that she was apprehensive. Shit, I was too. But I trusted myself and that was the driving force behind putting things into motion so quickly. Besides, if I say I'm going to do something then I'm going to do it. Knowing that Destinee was willing to trust me as much as I trusted myself, added a little pressure, but it also motivated me.

Within three hours of convincing Destinee, Amber had

let me know that the available unit in her complex was super cute so I applied and was approved to move in. Once it became official, I searched for recording studios in the area and even found an event space that I could rent out for casting calls for new *Frost* models. As far as mine and Destinee's cars went, I chose to have my car shipped so that Orien could hop on a flight with me as opposed to sitting in the car for hours -- I couldn't do that to my son. Destinee on the other hand decided that she would drive so that she wouldn't have to pay to have her car shipped there.

After I booked my flight, I sent a screenshot of my ticket to Eric just to show him how serious I was about the move. I really loved that we were still on speaking terms after our breakup. Like I said before, it really was a testament to how much I had grown over the years because in the past, once I was done with a man, he was dead to me. Anyway, Eric kept his word and bought furniture for me that was set to get to Atlanta the day after I would get there. The rest of my belongings were going to be moved by movers so I set up a moving company and picked up packing supplies for the big move. Destinee was able to pack all of her stuff into her car since she only had clothes and stuff like that. Things were moving fast and any sense of nervousness started to dissolve and a sense of hopefulness was taking over. I was excited to get away from the weight of everything that held me back in LA.

Even though my nerves about the move had gotten better, leaving my apartment behind was still a bittersweet feeling for me. What started off as a new beginning in that apartment ended as what felt like a tragedy but I masked those feelings because I didn't want Destinee to know that I was struggling. Besides that, it was the first moment where I thought that maybe it wasn't really a fresh start that I needed in order to fill the void I carried. I realized that maybe what I needed was deep healing but it was too late to turn back because I had already done so much to make the move happen in such a short period of time. Instead, I went back to my high school days. Remember when I would change my name every time I started a new school? Even though I was mostly known as Winter, some of the people close to me, still called me Kay so I decided that once I moved to Atlanta, *everybody* would have to call me Winter — no matter who it was.

DESTINEE and the movers left the day before my flight so that we would all arrive around the same time. Before she left, we made sure that she had hella snacks and energy drinks and stuff so that she could make the drive without having to spend extra money on hotel rooms. She also shared her location with me so that I would always know where she was in case something happened, but also so that she didn't have to text me every time I wanted to know what state she was driving through or how much longer it would take her.

Since Destinee left before I did, I slept in my empty apartment by myself that night and really reflected on my life. I was definitely battling depression but in the moments where my thoughts weren't dark, I always found a way to motivate myself. And since I was in that space, I reached out to a few promoters in Atlanta that I had interacted with on social media a few times to see if they had any events coming up. Even though I knew that I could probably hang out with Amber, I wanted to make sure that I was expanding my network as a whole. Partying was cool, but I wanted to meet more people in Atlanta so that I could start putting myself in different rooms as quickly as possible.

Crazy enough, one of the promoters hit me back saying

that he had a party coming up that he would love for me to host if I was down. The party was the next day, which was the same day I would be getting to Atlanta and it happened to be at one of the super lit strip clubs. Obviously I was down. Shit, I was just hitting him up to see if I could pull up in general so the fact that he wanted me to pull up and make some money made it even better. It felt like everything was working out in my favor. For once, my life felt like it was perfectly aligned with the vision I had for myself. I was very quickly coming up on my first night in a new city with only two friends and I had already closed a deal without even having to do any real work for it. I loved that for me. I couldn't wait to see Destinee to share the good news with her. Plus I knew that she was going to be down to party. Well, I also knew that she was going to be tired as fuck after that long ass drive, but we didn't have time to sleep. That's life.

My flight was scheduled early the next morning and Destinee ended up getting to Atlanta about an hour before I landed so she waited for Orien and I at the airport. Again, another thing that just worked out in my favor organically. When I told her about the hosting I had booked, she was excited for me but knew that she definitely needed to sleep for a few hours. She was tired as hell from the thirty-two hour car ride, so I drove us to our new apartment while she took a quick nap along the way.

When we finally pulled up at our new apartment, I screamed with joy which scared Orien and caused Destinee to jump out of her skin.

"Sorry, bitch! We're finally here! We made it!" I screamed.

Poor Destinee tried to snap herself out of the delirious state she was in to match my excitement.

"Ayyyyye!" She said, with no real enthusiasm.

The apartment complex as a whole looked exactly like the

photos I saw on the website and I mean, I knew that Amber wouldn't have been living there if it wasn't a nice building, but sometimes you just need to see shit for yourself. But anyway, even though Destinee was going to contribute to the rent each month, she wasn't going on the lease at all since my credit was better out of the two of us. I didn't want the landlord to have any speculation whatsoever so I parked in the future resident parking spot and Destinee stayed in the car while I met with the leasing manager to sign my lease, get the keys, and find out where our actual parking spots were located.

Once that was all settled, I was hype to go see the unit we'd be living in, but as soon as the leasing manager opened the door to our apartment I felt a rush of disappointment. The apartment was dark as fuck in the middle of the day. The thing about depression and poorly lit rooms is that it makes it easier for your brain to go to a dark place mentally, and that's really the last thing I needed. Don't get me wrong, I was grateful to have found a spot so quickly and easily but I just wished that Amber told me that it was so dark ahead of time. At least then I could have probably asked if there were any other units available that had better natural lighting or at the very least, prepared my mind for the lack of light my apartment had. Whatever the case, I signed off on the move-in paperwork and immediately went to let Destinee know that we could start moving in. She was just excited to take a nap and Orien was just excited to walk around freely. Me on the other hand? I was excited to be starting a whole new life.

Not too long after we unloaded all of Destinee's bags from her car, we received a call from the moving company that they wouldn't be arriving with the rest of my stuff for another twenty-four hours. Apparently they were having mechanical issues with the moving truck and had to wait for another truck to become available and then transfer my stuff from one truck to the other before they could finish out the job. Luckily Destinee had all of her stuff in her car and I had two suitcases full of clothing and hair and makeup stuff, so we weren't too stressed out about a one day delay. I was just going to have to work with whatever I had with me for the strip club that night and I was totally fine with that. When you're a bad bitch, you can wear whatever you want and still be a bad bitch. I don't make the rules.

Destinee slept almost the entire day, but I was too excited so I was up researching different recording studios Atlanta had to offer, writing in my journal, planning how I'd decorate the place, and I even went down to Amber's apartment to hang out with her for a bit. I invited her to the club with us, but she wasn't in the mood to go out.

LATER THAT NIGHT, the promoter sent a car for Destinee and I to be driven to the strip club. When we pulled up, the line for general admission was almost wrapped around the block and the valet lot was full of cars that made it clear that there was nothing but rich niggas inside. My promoter greeted us as we hopped out of the car and walked us inside, straight to the table. He knew ahead of time that it would just be Destinee and I since we had literally just landed that same day, so he placed us at his table because that's what made the most sense. It didn't matter to me as long as I was collecting a check at the end of the night.

About an hour into the night, Destinee and I were at the table minding our business, turning up and lit as fuck. We were taking shots, smacking asses, and making it rain with stacks of money that the promoter had given us to throw. As one of the dancers started giving me a lap dance, Destinee whispered in my ear.

"Here comes Kevin Campos." It wasn't much of a whisper considering how loud the music was.

Funny enough, I had randomly met Kevin a few years before that. Even though he lived in Atlanta, he had his birthday party in LA and I had gotten invited to it by someone that worked for him. At the time, I had no idea who he was but once we were introduced to one another, we instantly clicked. His vibe was hella cool and we had so much chemistry that it felt as though we had known each other for years. We literally danced and turned up together the entire night of his birthday but never spoke again after that. There was no specific reason we never spoke again, we just didn't and we lived in two different states so it really didn't matter much.

When Destinee told me that she saw him, I didn't really acknowledge her because I was enjoying my lap dance and basically just assumed that he'd be at a different table than we were at. It wasn't like I was going to go out of my way to say hi to him or anything. Plus, a couple years had passed since my last encounter with him so he was basically a stranger at that point.

By the time my lap dance ended, all of the dancers had cleared out from our table but to my surprise, Kevin and his people had made their way to the table. Destinee and I were in our own little world dancing with each other and having a good time.

Kevin interrupted by tapping my arm lightly. "Hey, how you doin'? I'm Kev." He smiled sarcastically.

Holding my hand out for him to shake it, I said, "Winter. Nice to meet you. This is Destinee." Meeting his sarcasm with my own.

"Nice to meet you." Kevin said as he shook Destinee's hand.

We all laughed and he reached over to hug me. "How you been, man? It's been a long time!"

Before I could answer he continued with, "What y'all drinkin'? I'm about to get a few more bottles."

Destinee didn't give me a chance to reply. She probably knew that I would say something slick.

"We're drinking tequila all night." She smiled.

"Bet." He said with confidence.

Kevin reached over and tapped the chest of one of the men he arrived with and then leaned in to say something to him. I can only assume that Kevin told the man what bottles to order because the man immediately searched the crowd until he found a bottle girl. Shortly after that, six bottle girls with sparklers, four bottles, stacks of money, and a sign that read *Kevin Campos* came dancing toward our table. Basically, the party had just gotten started.

The promoter brought a few more girls to the table and everyone was turning up, dancing and taking shots with each other. We were throwing so much money, you couldn't see the floor. Everyone was singing along to Kevin's songs whenever the DJ played them. It was a movie. Destinee and I were super lit at this point. Like, so lit that we started kissing each other, I mean you never got a little too drunk and started kissing your homegirl? Anyways, I don't remember how it happened but somehow Kevin became involved in the little freaky situation we had going on. We were doing the absolute most and she kept saying that we should have a threesome with Kevin.

Now, I'll keep it real with you, I was super lit so I was down for all the bullshit, but even with how lit I was, it wasn't lost on me that Destinee had ONLY been kissing me the whole night. For somebody that wanted a threesome with me *and* Kevin, she wasn't really giving Kevin any type of play. She was literally only rubbing on my ass and kissing on me which I really only paid attention to because in the past, our friends would always tell me that Destinee was gay for me. Random, I know. Whenever it would come up, they would always joke that she wanted to be my boyfriend and I would always laugh it off because I never saw what they saw. As far as I was concerned, she was my best friend who loved me the same way I loved her; as a friend.

Even with all of that in the back of my drunken mind, I still agreed to the threesome. We all ended up leaving the club after I got my money from the promoter and headed back to Kevin's place. He put Destinee and I in a different car than him and his people for obvious reasons – to keep people out of our business.

When we got to his place, we wasted no time and he led us straight to his bedroom.

THE NEXT MORNING, I woke up on the floor of my new apartment surrounded by blankets and the one pillow that was able to fit into my carry-on bag. For a moment I was confused on how I had gotten home and then I remembered that Kevin wanted us to spend the night at his house but I made him get a car to take us home instead. He was a nice guy and Destinee and I obviously had a good time with him, but I wasn't trying to sleep in that man's bed. I laid in my nest of blankets trying to remember what had happened after we all went into Kevin's room but all I could remember was Destinee telling me "I don't want him, I only want you."

I realized that my body was aching from sleeping on the floor and my head was pounding from all of the tequila we drank so I decided to forget trying to remember the night and focused on surviving my hangover. Besides the hangover, I was so happy to be in a new city, and after the night I had, I knew that Atlanta was going to be a different kind of lit. Orien was curled up next to me so I made sure to give him some love until I was interrupted by my phone blowing up with texts from Eric. Basically, he was telling me that the furniture he ordered for me wasn't going to arrive for another week.

I was so hungover that I couldn't manage to reply right away. Plus, you know that recapping a lit night with your girls is always first on the list no matter how hungover you are, so of course Orien and I hopped up and made our way into Destinee's room. She was still sleeping and normally I would have done something annoying like slid myself under the blankets with her or something like that but it didn't feel like the right thing to do after the night we had just had. If my friends were right and Destinee really was gay for me, I didn't want to send her any mixed signals. I didn't want her to think that what we might have done the night before was going to be a regular thing and I didn't want her to think that she and I could be anything more than friends. Instead, I placed Orien on top of her back as she was bundled up under her blanket.

"Winter. No. The last time you woke me up, we moved across the country. Leave me alone bitch." Destinee pulled the blanket over her head and turned her back to me.

"Ok and we got here and had the time of our lives immediately. So, obviously I was right. Just like always." I said through laughter.

"Bitch. Last night was turnt. And I actually got Kevin's number this time." I laughed.

That woke her right up. "Oh. Ok. Turn you up." Destinee said, with less excitement than I thought she'd have.

Orien jumped as Destinee shifted her body into a sitting position and I sat down as well.

"I'm happy we ran into him. I forgot that I clicked with

him like that. And he's here in Atlanta which is even better. He's cool. I fuck with him." I explained.

Destinee stood up and began to fold her blankets.

I'm not going to lie, I didn't love her energy but I didn't put too much thought into it because I had woken her up after a crazy night, so I understood.

I continued, "We moved to Atlanta for something new and fresh, that's exactly what I'm trying to do. I'm not trying to hop into a relationship or no shit like that, I just think Kevin is cool and I'm sure he can plug me with producers and shit too."

"Yeah, I feel you." Destinee said as she placed her folded blanket in the corner of her room. "We need to change our lives with some furniture." She laughed.

Standing up, I said, "Girl. I know. Eric texted me this morning saying that our shit is about to take a whole week to get here. But the other stuff will still be here today."

"Perfect." She smiled.

"I'm going to hit Amber and see what she's doing today!" I said as I walked out of Destinee's room.

As I walked down the hall into my room, I FaceTimed Amber to tell her that she had missed out on a lit ass night, but I made sure to leave out the part that Destinee and I had ended up back at Kevin's place. While we were on the phone, I ended up telling her that my furniture delivery got pushed back a week and immediately she offered me a brand new spare mattress that she had. The mattress would be perfect because my body was already sore and I was not trying to sleep on the floor for another night, yet alone another week. As soon as I hung up with Amber, Destinee and I went down the hall to her apartment and brought the mattress back to our place.

A week later, my furniture had finally arrived so Destinee and I were able to fully decorate the apartment. I was excited to throw out the mattress Amber had given me and finally sleep on my own bed. I made sure to buy extra lamps so that I could add as much light to the place as possible. It was finally starting to feel more like a home rather than just some abandoned apartment we were staying in.

3

LAST BEACON OF HOPE

BESIDES THE BRIEF delay from the moving and the furniture companies, everything was going great in Atlanta. Amber and I started to spend more time together and Kevin and I actually started kickin' it and talking everyday. I was really starting to like him. The best part was that one of my goals before we moved to Atlanta was to find a new model for my online store, *Frost,* and I accomplished that within the first month of me being there. About fifty girls showed up to my casting call and a lot of them were beautiful but there was this girl named Lindsay that was tall as hell with long, black hair, beautiful eyes, and a bomb ass body that stuck out to me the most. I couldn't pinpoint her race but she looked White and Mexican. Lindsay's vibe was hella cool and she wasn't in there acting super boujee like a lot of the other models were so she stood out to me.

When Destinee and I interviewed her, we learned that she was a stripper and obviously since that's my background as well, I was pretty much sold on picking her before I even got through the rest of the girls. As a matter of fact, I called her as soon as the casting was over to let her know that she had booked the job. I love pretty bitches who hustle and don't think they're too good for anybody. She seemed to have a good head on her shoulders too. She didn't share all of her business with us, but she had goals and a desire to get out of the strip club and that was another reason I really wanted to hire her. Yeah, it wasn't a huge gig, but I knew from experience how even the smallest step in the direction of your dreams could be enough motivation to keep going.

Over the next few months, Lindsay started to hang out with us more often. Whenever I would host events I'd bring her, Amber, and Destinee with me and whenever Amber would come over to chill with Destinee and I, I'd invite Lindsay over too. Out of all of us, Amber was the only one with a boyfriend at the time and they lived together, so she'd be the one to leave events early or leave my house whenever her man would get back home. You know how that shit goes. But one night, Lindsay had us playing this drinking game she made up that basically forced you to choose a dare or take a double shot and when it was Amber's turn, she chose *dare*.

"Ooo! Dare?! Ok, girl!" Lindsay was shocked to hear Amber choose dare. "Ok, I dare you to kiss Winter."

Amber was sitting on the couch and I was sitting on the floor right next to her legs. She looked over at Lindsay and laughed and then looked down at me as if to get my permission. I didn't say a word, I just laughed.

"Oh, grow up!" Amber said as she leaned over the couch and grabbed my face.

Amber and I actually started kissing and it was more intense than I had anticipated for it to be. Like I thought she was just going to give me a little high school pop kiss, but she was giving me a full blown kiss like she was my man.

"Damn! I feel like I need to tell Kevin I'm over here cheating on him!" I said jokingly when the kiss was over.

All of the girls laughed.

Destinee interrupted our laughter, "So Kevin is your man now?" She asked as if she was spilling some tea.

"Girl, bye. I'm just kidding." I laughed.

Amber cut in, "Ok, bitch but y'all have been spending a lot of time together. You with that nigga like every day."

Lindsay filled everyone's cup up with more tequila while Destinee and Amber tried to figure out my relationship status.

Before taking the shot Lindsay had just poured into my cup I said, "We definitely spend a lot of time together. I fuck with him for sure. But until he literally asks me to be his girlfriend, I'm not claiming no nigga that's not claiming me." I grabbed my cup.

"Please." Lindsay said. "If y'all are doing relationship things, y'all are definitely a couple. Fuck the bullshit." And then she took her shot.

"We're not but we'll see. It's only been a few months." I laughed. "Y'all so damn nosey!"

And you know what, now that I think of it, the only time Destinee was really a part of that conversation was when she started it. After that, she never said another word. Anyway, the rest of the night was cool. Lindsay ended up sleeping over because she was too drunk to drive home and Amber must have gone home after I fell asleep. The next morning, she called me.

"Hey, girl. When you have time, can you bring that mattress back over here?" She said as soon as I answered the phone.

"Damn, I been got rid of that. All the new shit came and I threw out the one you gave me." I almost felt bad.

"Oh. Ok. It's cool, John said that you've probably been fucking hella niggas on it anyway so he didn't even want me to ask for it back." She said nonchalantly.

My face twisted up at that weird sideways ass comment.

First of all, it was too fucking early for that shit. But second of all, why even call if you didn't actually want it back? People just be doing strange shit for no reason.

Anyway, I said, "Not that it's John's business because I don't know why your nigga would be concerned about who I'm fucking, but no I haven't. I don't know what you think this is but stop playing with me."

She met my attitude with her own. "Girl, it was just a joke. Why are you getting offended if it's not true? I'm not about to deal with nobody's attitude this early in the morning."

Amber hung up in my face and that was basically the end of our friendship. Come to find out, she had told her man about us being drunk and making out the night before and I guess he was bothered that she didn't "bring me home for a threesome". Basically just like any other weak man that doesn't get his way, I became all types of hoes in his mind. It'll always be funny to me that a man that I wouldn't let fuck me on my worst day, would ever fix his mouth to call me a hoe. How would you know that I'm a hoe if you could never fuck? I don't know why Amber even bothered to tell him about the kiss because it was just some drunk shit anyway.

Whatever the case, Amber was my first friendship gone bad in Atlanta but I was focused on my goals so I wasn't even worried about it. Plus, I had other shit to worry about. Kevin and I were actually getting a lot closer but we were beefing a lot too. I would spend nights at a time at his house, go to the studio with him, we'd go to different events together, all types of shit. Destinee would spend a lot of time at his house with me too. I know you're probably thinking like, bitch, why would you have your best friend around your man after y'all had a threesome?! But honestly, I didn't see anything wrong with it. The way I was looking at it was like, Destinee and I had never spoken about that night after it happened and Kevin and I decided that threesomes wouldn't play a role in our situation. So we were all on the same page in my book. And don't forget that from what I could remember, Destinee didn't even touch Kevin that night. She was really more concerned about me than she was about him. So I was thinking like, yeah, she saw his dick and watched him fuck me but that was it. Kevin wasn't my nigga for real, but that was still my nigga, you know what I'm saying?

I've never been one to beg a man to be with me, but I really fucked with Kevin and he really fucked with me. There were two major issues though. One was that Kevin was cheap as fuck and that was a turnoff considering the fact that I hadn't been with a man that was cheap since I was a damn teenager. But the other issue was that I was still fighting off major depression. Even though I had come out of the dark place where I wanted to kill myself, I hadn't actually dealt with any of the things that made me feel that way and secretly, it was all still weighing me down. I was drowning my pain in liquor and silencing my thoughts at parties. At first, it was easy for me to use hosting as my excuse for partying and drinking so much. But when Kevin would find out that I was partying at other niggas' tables and flirting and shit, he would have an issue with it. My drinking eventually became an issue too because I would start fights with him every time I was drunk.

There was never any real reason for me to go out partying and drinking as much as I was because it wasn't like I was desperate for the money, but it was a fun, easy, and secret escape for me. No one, including Kevin, knew that I was struggling as much as I was. Unfortunately, it was forcing us to keep each other at a distance. Kevin had a good heart though. He and I were alike in so many ways it was crazy. He loved *Erykah Badu*, just like I did and we would really vibe off that. His creativity sparked mine, the way mine sparked his. Yeah, he would mention that I was too chaotic and that I lived too wild of a life for him, but he was able to balance me out and that was something that I really loved about him.

One night, I pulled up to his studio session like I always did and he wanted to play a song for me. Like I said already, we spent hella time at the studio together so it wasn't the first time he wanted to play me a song, and he was super talented so I always loved listening to his shit. That night was a little different, though. The song was basically about him not being sure if a girl was fucking with him for his money or not and him not being able to fuck with her how he wanted to because she had too much going on in her life. In the song, he basically goes on to say that she's perfect for him but he can't give his love to her like he wants to because it would be crazy to do something like that. It was pretty much all the same shit he was telling me in real life.

As soon as the song was over I was like, "Is this about me?" I already knew the answer to my question.

Kevin laughed and then he said, "Yeah, but only the chorus."

First of all, it pissed me off that he thought it was funny but the fact that he wrote a song that basically said he didn't know if I was fucking with his cheap ass for his money and that he couldn't love me because I had too much going on had me livid. It was a smack in the face because we had spent so much time together and that song basically felt like he was telling me we would never be together. I was so real with Kevin. I know that I was doing the most when I would drink too much and cause arguments, but I always apologized for that. And yes, hella niggas were on me when I would go out but that's a small price to pay when you fuck with a bad bitch. So to write that song, record it, and then sit in my face and laugh about it felt disrespectful.

After he laughed like it was a fucking joke to play that song for me, Kevin and I got in a big ass argument so I left the studio and went home. It was yet another thing to add to my long list of things that had me fucked up. I was just tired of feeling betrayed by the people that meant something to me. I was tired of people saying and doing whatever the fuck they wanted to me and thinking shit was sweet after. I've always let shit slide for way too long. Kevin should have left me the fuck alone if he felt like I was too much for him, not write a song about why he can't be with me and then think everything would be normal after that. What the fuck?

That night, I told myself that I was done with Kevin. We weren't a real couple and I wasn't about to give him another chance to play in my face. Of course, my feelings were hurt so I wanted to just get away for a few days without dealing with his bullshit. I decided last minute that I was going to meet a few of my girls in Miami. It was a trip that they had already planned months before and initially, I told them I wouldn't be able to make it but with Kevin working my last damn nerve and *Frost* doing so well, I thought I deserved a quick, cute little getaway.

The group of girls that I was meeting in Miami was a group of girls that Destinee didn't know. She wasn't trying to spend money to go be in the faces of a bunch of bitches she didn't know so she stayed in Atlanta. It made no difference to me because I was ready to turn up and forget about Kevin regardless.

My second night in Miami, I was super turnt, so obviously I called my best friend because I missed her already. Destinee didn't answer when I called, but it wasn't a big deal because she obviously didn't have to answer the phone every single time I called her. I was just curious to know what she could have been doing seeing as though she didn't know anyone in Atlanta besides Amber, Lindsay and a couple of distant cousins. Since she was still sharing her location with me from way back when we moved to Atlanta, I figured I'd check it real quick and then go on about my business until she called me back.

You want to take a wild guess where her location was? Ding, ding, ding! Kevin's house. At first, I thought that I was trippin' because I was so drunk but we all know that you sober up real quick when shit hits the fan. I must have called Destinee's phone five times before she finally texted me back. A TEXT. But you know me, I'm going to get my issue off regardless, so I texted her back asking her why the fuck she was at Kevin's house. She told me that he was having a party and I didn't even bother replying because that was all I needed to know. You better believe that I was on a flight out of Miami the very next morning. The entire flight I went over how I was going to approach the situation and decided that I just needed to remain as calm as possible. When I got home that afternoon, Destinee was sitting on the couch watching TV as if shit was sweet which low key almost pissed me off more.

As soon as the front door closed, I pressed her. "Why were you at Kevin's house? That's hella weird." I sounded calm as fuck but I was pissed.

Destinee was my best friend, so I knew that I would know whether or not she was lying when she answered the question.

"He was having a party. Why else would I be there?" She said with an attitude.

The fact that she said, *'why else would I be there'*, really pissed me off even more because no bitch, *'why would you go there'*, was the real question. Destinee knew that me and Kevin were beefing because the night that I left the studio after hearing the song, I told her everything when I got home! Therethefuckfore, she shouldn't have been over there.

And to be honest with you, I wouldn't have cared that she went if she would have just told me beforehand, instead of doing it behind my back and then having an attitude when I asked about it. It's the principle for me.

Destinee and I argued for like twenty minutes. It was back and forth name calling over, and over again. Which is stupid to me because, how do you go to my niggas house without me and still find a way to argue with me about it? Nothing surprises me anymore. During the argument she kept threatening to leave and move back to LA. Shit like that doesn't scare me so I told her that she could get the fuck out right then. She wasn't expecting me to basically kick her out but if you're going to threaten to leave me with our apartment simply because you know you're not on the lease, I'm going to act like this is only my shit too. Therefore, get out MY HOUSE.

Destinee ended up packing a bag and leaving almost immediately to sleep at one of her distant cousins' houses. She was dumb enough to threaten to leave me with our apartment alone and trifling enough to go to my nigga's house without telling me so I didn't give a fuck where she went. Sure enough, the next morning she came back to the apartment, packed up all of her belongings and drove back to LA. Her crazy ass didn't even bother saying a word to me before she left. Even though I knew that meant I'd have to start paying for our apartment fully on my own I didn't try to stop her because I've never been the type to beg a bitch for anything. Anyway, obviously I ended shit with Kevin but I told you I was already done with him in my mind way before that.

I know that I always act like I don't care about shit, but it's obvious that I do. I was really disappointed in Destinee. She was my best friend. She knew exactly what I had gone through in my life, I looked out for her in so many ways, and she knew that I wouldn't have been cool with her going to Kevin's house while I was fighting with him. The fact that she did it anyway really tore me apart. This doesn't make it right, but I expect men to fuck up or do some bullshit. Men don't know or adhere to the same principle of trust and loyalty that women do and Destinee betrayed that principle by deliberately failing to tell me that she was going to go to his house.

The night after Destinee left, is when the pain finally set in, and my thoughts had become dark again. My heart was broken yet again but by someone who I didn't even know was capable of betraying me the way Destinee did. I couldn't believe I was back to being alone and back to being heartbroken. I couldn't believe that yet another friend had betrayed me and another man had hurt me.

THAT NIGHT, my thoughts became darker than they ever had before and I felt completely empty inside. For the next four days, I barely ate anything, I didn't talk to anyone or leave my apartment for anything. The only reason I would take showers was because I wanted to give Orien a break from watching me cry all day, every day. I wanted to die. I know it seems like this incident wasn't serious enough to want to do all of that, but it was more than just Destinee and Kevin. It was years of unhealed trauma that came flooding back. There was nothing inside of me that wanted to live any longer but I didn't want to leave Orien all alone. I didn't want him to starve to death. I didn't want him to feel like I abandoned him. After four days of not sleeping and barely eating, I started to become delusional. So much so that there were voices in my head telling me to kill myself. The voices were loud, clear, and scary. They were adamant about me taking my life. They gave me a number of ways I could accomplish it and they were starting to sound like they were right.

I had finally become so afraid of myself that I called three of my homegirls and not one of them answered. What's funny is that I went four days without talking to anyone and not one person sent a text or called me to make sure everything was ok. So those voices, the ones telling me that I didn't deserve to live, the ones telling me that I was unworthy of love, the ones encouraging me to kill myself, were starting to get closer to the finish line.

I gave myself one last beacon of hope and decided to call my mother. It had been months since I had spoken to her but she answered on the first ring and for the first few seconds of the phone call, all I could do was cry into the phone. When I finally mustered up the courage to tell her what was going on, she immediately booked a flight for me to go back home to the Bay. It sounds crazy to say this but Orien's life meant more to me than my own life in that moment and it gave me the strength to block out the sound of the voices in my head just long enough for my mom to save me.

4

SOLITARY CONFINEMENT

ON THE PLANE ride to the Bay, I was basically a zombie. Going from not sleeping for four days straight and hearing voices in my head that were telling me to kill myself to hopping on a flight, had me feeling like I wasn't even in my body. You know how when you're driving and you're so deep in your thoughts that you can't remember whether or not you stopped at red lights on the way to wherever you were going? That's how I felt. I knew that I had done all that I was supposed to do in order to get to the Bay, because I was there, but I didn't really remember doing any of it. When my mom picked me up from the airport, I remember she got out of the car and gave me the tightest hug ever but I don't actually remember walking to her car.

When I got to my mom's house, the first thing I did was take a shower. I turned the water to the hottest temperature possible and stood under the water and just cried. The shower at my mom's house was no stranger to my tears, you know I cried plenty of tears in there throughout my teenage years. In a way I felt at home even in the middle of my darkest depression. I was angry with myself for letting everything I went through cause me so much pain that I wanted to die. I knew I was stronger than that. I knew that I was capable of so much more. I knew that I deserved a life full of happiness, love, and luxury. Instead, I didn't want a life at all and I hated that that's what everything had come to. My life was obviously in shambles and as much as I wanted all of the pain to go away, as much as I wanted better for myself, as much as I wanted to get out of that shower, and get back on my shit, I felt like I couldn't. I felt like I didn't have the strength; not mentally, or physically. But I promised myself that once I got out of the shower, I wouldn't cry anymore. I promised myself that I would get out my feelings and figure out how to get back on my shit.

For the next few days, all I did was sleep. It was literally the only thing I had energy for after not being able to sleep for days. I don't know if you know, but bitch, mental exhaustion is a whole different type of exhaustion. Shit, I couldn't even really eat anything. My mom would try her best to get me to eat every day and make sure there was food in the kitchen when she left for work, but I didn't really have an appetite and I could barely hold anything down. When I did finally start eating, I was eating junk – like fast food or gas station snacks, I had no appetite or will to cook.

It took about a week for me to start feeling like myself again. All of the friends I called when I was ready to kill myself had called me back, but I didn't answer any of their calls. I just sent them text messages telling them I was too busy to talk and would hit them when I was back in Atlanta. Since none of them answered when I called originally, none of them needed to hear what was going on in my life. It wasn't beef or anything, I just didn't want anyone to know. In a way I was embarrassed that I had fallen into such a dark, vulnerable place and admitting that I need help can be hard for me sometimes.

While I was in the Bay, I spent time with my cousins and a few of my homegirls; really on some "getting back to my roots" type shit. As far as they knew, I was just back home for a minute to spend time with my family. Eventually, I started to make my way back onto social media too. The break was cool, but I had to get back to business and continue to promote my store and shit. You know ya girl is going to make money no matter what city I'm in, so when I started posting on social media again, a promoter from the Bay hit me asking if I'd be interested in hosting anytime soon. That obviously worked out considering I was already out there. I ended up hosting a party and me, my cousins, and a couple of my homegirls went out and turned the city up. Hosting the club brought me back to life, and after that, I felt like I was ready to go back to Atlanta so I booked a flight for a few days later.

Pretty much immediately after booking my flight back to Atlanta, I coincidentally got a message from some nigga named Jerome Jackson that played football there. To keep it real with you, he was low key ugly. Like, before I replied to his message, I was looking at his photos thinking *damn, this nigga looks like a fruit bat* but he actually sounded like he had some sense in his message, so I replied. Whatever, I didn't think it was that big of a deal. Anyway, we started messaging back and forth every day and I fucked with him because he was just so easy to talk to. He held great conversations and didn't come off thirsty or entitled like a lot of rich niggas do when they slide in my DM's. You'd be surprised how much of a challenge it is for men to actually approach a woman with some respect when they send their lame ass messages. Part of that is because there are bitches out there that accept dust for attention which makes men believe every woman is willing to tolerate that bullshit, but that's a different story for a different time. I say all of that to say that Jerome was like a breath of fresh air. Especially since I was just starting to feel like the boss bitch that I am again.

LEAVING the Bay was harder than I expected it to be because my mom was still worried about me. She was trying to get me to stay a little longer but I knew that I was good and there were things I needed to get done in Atlanta. The first thing I did when I got back was deep clean my apartment. I wanted to not only get rid of Destinee's negative energy, but I also wanted to get rid of my own negative energy. Anything or anybody that fucked with the peace of mind I felt at the time, was no longer welcome in my space.

The day after I got back to Atlanta, I kicked it with Lindsay. Even though she started out as a model for my store, she had actually started to become one of my actual friends. She was real and unproblematic and that was, and still is, the type of person that I love having in my circle. Lindsay and I kept it really simple. We got cute to got out for dinner and drinks. The entire night Lindsay shared pieces of her life with me that she had never shared with me before and it made me fuck with her even more because she had a lot of situations that were similar to mine in her life. I didn't share what I had just gone through with her, because it was still fresh and I still wasn't ready for anyone to know, but I did share things from my childhood with her. It was cool getting to know her on a deeper level, especially since I didn't have many friends in Atlanta. At that point, I felt like Atlanta was starting to feel like home.

When I woke up the next day, it was time for me to get back on my shit. I ate breakfast, did some inventory shopping for my store and then booked some studio time for that night. Jerome had messaged me to see how I was and had finally asked if he could take me out to dinner and low key, I was excited to say yes. He had a cool little vibe and we connected pretty well so I was looking forward to spending time with him just to see if that connection translated the same in person. Sometimes people are cool when you talk to them in text messages or over the phone, but have trash personalities in real life. Anyway, we decided that we would link that night before my studio session so I spent the rest of my day at the mall looking for an outfit to wear.

I ended up wearing a white bodysuit with a pair of white jeans that fit like a glove, and heels. I always feel like a bad bitch in white and I wanted my outfit to work for dinner and the studio without me having to change in between. Jerome offered to pick me up from my house but I told him that I would meet him at the restaurant because I was going to go straight to the studio when we were done.

He got to the restaurant before I did, so the hostess walked me right to our table and I was shocked as hell to see that he was actually fine as fuck. The little fruit bat that I saw on social media was actually a fine ass chocolate man that was like six foot one with a nice body who was very clearly just not photogenic. I felt like I was on a blind date because we had only been talking in the DM's before that. We never exchanged numbers or FaceTimed or anything but I was happy to see him. Secretly, I was happy that he wasn't as ugly as I thought he was because I liked what I knew of him so the fact that he was actually cute, made everything so much better.

Dinner was perfect. You know I love me some good food and good conversation and that was exactly what Jerome and I had. We laughed together all night like we had already known each other for years. We were both kind of bothered that I had a studio session after dinner because he had plans to go to the club with his boys later that night and wanted me to pull up with him so that we could spend more time together. My session was only booked for four hours, so I told him that I'd hit him afterwards to see where he was at and if he still wanted me to pull up, I would.

MY STUDIO SESSION WAS BOMB. I started writing a song to a beat that I already had for a while and I was excited to start recording it. My mind was already putting together different cover shoot ideas and different ways to get the song to the DJ's in Atlanta once it was ready. After the session, I called Jerome, since we had finally exchanged numbers at dinner.

"Hey. What's up? I just finished my session." For some reason, I was nervous.

He was excited to hear from me. "Hi, beautiful. How was it?" He asked.

I was flattered that he asked. "It went well. I'm excited to be back in the studio." I said.

"Ok! I see you. Well, I have a car picking me up in like an hour to go to the club. You still feel like coming out with me tonight?" At that point, he was the one that was nervous.

"Yeah, I'm down. I feel like we need to celebrate life!" I laughed.

Jerome had no idea what the last month of my life was like but it really felt like a victory for me to be in the mental space that I was in. A month before meeting him, I was literally thinking about ways to kill myself and there I was in true Winter fashion pushing through and bossing up at the same time. A celebration was most definitely necessary. Without knowing what we were really celebrating, Jerome agreed and told me to meet him at his house so that we could just ride together. I'm not going to lie, at first, I wanted to tell him that

I would just meet him at the club because I wasn't trying to go to his house. You know like I know, men can be disgusting humans sometimes and can flip the script real quick. I didn't want us meeting at his house to turn into no weird shit.

Needless to say, I ended up meeting him at his house anyway. I mean, he was a whole NFL player – what was he going to do, kidnap me? When I pulled up, the house was as beautiful as I expected it to be. Jerome was waiting at the front door while I parked my car.

"The car service will be here in about fifteen minutes. You want to come in and have a drink or chill out here until then?" He asked as I walked toward him.

I wasn't thrilled but I kept it cool. "Ok, cool. Let's have a drink then. That's fine." I said with a smile on my face.

Jerome gave me a hug before we went inside of his house and he smelled so fucking good. He had never given me any creeper vibes and I didn't genuinely think that inviting me to his house was some creep shit, I'm just being my dramatic self. Anyway, the inside of his house was even prettier than the outside but Jerome led us right to the kitchen so I didn't get a chance to look around.

"What you drinkin'?" He asked.

"Uhm. Oh. Wow. You just got a whole ass bar over there." I laughed as I saw his full wet bar. "Let's do tequila." I said as I sat down on a stool at the bar.

While he was pouring shots, I was looking around the kitchen wondering what the rest of the house looked like so I eventually told him to give me a tour. He showed me the guest bedrooms, the backyard, the game room – everything. There was one last door that he didn't show me and my nosey ass insisted that we tour that room, too.

"Wait. We forgot this room. I need the grand luxe tour." I said jokingly.

Jerome said, "Nah, you're not ready for this room yet. This room is for grown folks."

"Sir, please. You can't show me nothin' I haven't seen already, I'm sure. We only have like five minutes before the car gets here so hurry up!" I said.

"Don't say I didn't warn you." Jerome said with a mischievous smile as he opened the mystery door.

Bitch, the room was full of all types of sex toys like dildos, lube, whips, chains and all kinds of shit. It was so fuckin' weird but it was also fucking hilarious. Like, you would never think that Jerome Jackson had a sex room on some *'Fifty Shades of Gray'* type shit.

I was cracking the fuck up. "Oh my God. I was not expecting this!"

Jerome laughed too. "Well, shit. I told you it was a grown folks room. It don't get much more grown than this!"

I could tell that he was relieved I wasn't freaked out.

Lucky for both of us, he got a notification that our car was outside so we rushed back to the kitchen, took another shot, and then made our way to the club to meet up with his friends.

———

NOW, you know I don't ever care about a man's status or what he does for a living. It's never been about fame or money but based on who I had already dated in the past and having my own stuff popping, I always ended up with a man who had a bag. With that being said, based on who I knew Jerome was, I expected that there would probably be a few hating ass bitches in the club when they saw me with him, but I wasn't worried. Why would I be worried about a hater when I'm rich, lit, and pretty? Despite all that, me, Jerome and his friends were turning up and the girls that weren't at our table were up-fucking-set about it. You would have thought I stole him right out of their beds. By the end of the night, I had messages from pages that were obviously fake, calling me all types of hoes and gold diggers but I didn't care. Anyone who had common sense knew that neither of those things were true about me. I never went in search of "gold" from a man but somehow it always found me, so who was I to tell a rich nigga "beat it"?

It wasn't until weeks later that I found out that the reason bitches were so mad that I was out with Jerome was because he never took women out in public with him. I was like the first girl people saw him outside with and that shit ate people up. Do you know how insane you have to be in order to be upset that someone is literally just living their life? It was hilarious to me that they were so mad because they had no idea that we hadn't even known each other for very long. By the time I learned that information, we were already damn near inseparable. We had been spending hella time together. Going out all the time. He would chill at the studio with me from time to time. I was at his games. All types of shit. We were starting to get closer and closer and it felt good to connect with a new man.

Jerome was like a best friend and my boo all in one because he would gossip with me about shit all the time and we had the same warped sense of humor, but he also had some bomb ass dick and spoiled the fuck out of me. Balance, if you will. Bitches were still mad that he fucked with me and not them which will never not be funny. I take that back, it stopped being funny when I started getting messages from fake pages saying that Jerome was on the DL. Yup. Bitches hated us being together so much that they started accusing him of being a down low man. If you don't know what a "down low" man is, well, basically it's a boy who likes boys … but on the low. Get it?

Obviously I was no stranger to internet bullshit so I didn't even pay attention to any of it. Plus, he was fucking me so good there was no way in hell he was gay. We had a really good relationship. There were hardly, if ever, any disagreements. We never argued. He was never disrespectful and I never felt like he was moving greasy. But for some reason, shit just felt too good to be true. If you look back at my record, anything that has ever gone really good in my life, was always too good to be true and I was at a place where I wanted to know what the flaws were before I fell too deep with that man.

The messages weren't bothering me, but they were actually making me look at him a little differently. For example, the fact that he would gossip with me instead of saying shit like 'that's crazy' like other guys do when you're telling them some shit they don't care about was one thing. Another thing I thought about was his sex room and how he liked using sex toys when we would fuck. I knew I wasn't going to allow no hatin' ass bitch to come between me and Jerome, but I was definitely going to start paying attention just to see if the math was mathing.

One night while he was in the shower, I was in his bed watching TV and decided to go through his phone. This was big for me cause a bitch has PTSD okay? I don't normally go through phones or social media accounts unless I'm trying to lose ten pounds. Shit like that will leave you not eating for a week. I was expecting to catch him flirting with other bitches on social media or getting naked pictures sent to him. You know, shit that would show me exactly why I felt as though it was too good to be true. Instead, I found out way more than I ever thought I would. There weren't any bitches with their pussy busted wide open in his phone. No. Instead, Jerome was flirting with a man. There was a man sending him dick pics and ass shots and he was basically gagging over those photos the same way a man would gag over nudes from a woman. I was completely shocked. Honestly, I couldn't even believe it was real.

At first, I just put his phone back onto the side table and sat there in silence. Looked like that diet I told you about was starting that day. It took me a second to really process everything I saw and wrap my head around the fact that every message I had gotten about him being on the DL was in fact true. After a few minutes of processing, I went back through my messages to read them again and compare what they were saying to what I had seen. My mind was all over the fucking place. Crazy enough, I was more upset with myself for missing all of the signs than I was at him for being on the DL. I should've known by the way he loved to gossip with me and the way he would get "offended" by anything gay. I mean we lived in Atlanta for christ sake, you can't be homophobic in Atlanta.

Actually, I wasn't mad at him for being gay or bi at all. I was mad at him for betraying me. I was mad at him for using me as a prop to live out his lie. I just felt like if he was "bi" he should have told me but he went behind my back and had me looking like a fool. It was obviously not as much of a secret as he thought it was if I was getting messages about it, so he could have given me a heads up. Listen, I'm not saying it's easy for a Black man that is a professional athlete to live in his truth, but I am for sure saying that I didn't deserve to be played with.

When he got out of the shower, I was doing my best to just ignore everything I had just seen. My plan was just to tell him that I didn't think we should fuck with each other anymore and then just leave. I didn't want to embarrass him or give him the opportunity to lie to me, I just wanted to be done. My feelings were hurt and I didn't want to give another man the satisfaction of seeing me hurt again. But when he kissed me, I lost it.

"Don't fucking kiss me!" I said as I pushed him away from me and hopped out of the bed.

He was confused. "What happened?" He said as he held his towel in place.

"*What happened?* Are you serious? You tell me, Jerome? What fucking happened?" I didn't even bother looking at him while I aggressively threw my stuff into my overnight bag.

"I didn't do shit. So I don't know. I'm not about to play no guessing games." He was nonchalant.

His nonchalance pissed me off more. "Oh. So you don't think telling a nigga that sends you dick pics that you can't wait to see him again is nothing?" I laughed sarcastically and shook my head in disbelief. "Ok. You got it. Fuck you, Jerome."

Jerome didn't say anything at first. I could almost see his brain trying to assess the situation so that he could figure out a lie that would make sense.

"Why the fuck are you going through my phone?" He yelled. Loud.

That was all I needed to hear. I didn't need an explanation for his actions. I didn't need an apology. And I for damn sure didn't need his lies.

I took a deep breath as I placed the strap of my bag over my shoulder. "I just caught you in some freaky shit with a man and the only thing that you can do is ask me why I went through your phone? You're insane, Jerome. You're absolutely insane." I was super calm.

I walked out of his house and he didn't even try to stop me. This let down was different. I cared about Jerome. A lot. I was falling for him and I thought he was falling for me too. I didn't understand how I had missed all of the signs or why he chose me as a cover up.

I drove away from the house filled with so much confusion that I had to pull over on the side of the road and cry. Maybe I'm the one that was actually insane because after about five minutes of crying, I started cracking up. I was laughing because I couldn't believe that shit was real. I was laughing because some part of me felt good that he was messing around on me with a man and not a woman. I was laughing because I was glad that I had found out about it before I was in too deep with that man. I was laughing because I knew that there was no way in hell that anybody would believe me if I told them what I saw in that damn phone.

5

NEW NIGGA, WHO DIS?

IT DIDN'T TAKE me long to get over the whole Jerome situation because for one, there isn't much for me to do with a man that also likes men unless he's going to be honest about it. For two, I dropped *my single, "Ratchet Pussy"* which was the song I was working on when Jerome and I first met. I knew the song title was ghetto but that's exactly what the song was about --ghetto love and how you'll never get better love than the love you get from a ghetto bitch. It felt so good to finally drop new music after all the bullshit I had to go through to even get into a studio again, so there was no way a breakup would be the reason I couldn't enjoy releasing my song. I mean, at the end of the day, music is always and will always be my first love.

The same day that I released *"Ratchet Pussy"*, a promoter reached out to me to see if I wanted to host a Single Release party at his club. You know that shit was an easy 'yes' for me because it meant I was going to get paid for hosting an event, have my song played in the club, and turn up all at once. I still only had about three friends in Atlanta but the clubs were always turnt and I also felt like having my song played in the club was going to be a real good look for me. Hearing your shit in the studio is cool. Running a car test on your shit is necessary. But hearing your shit in the club and watching people catch a vibe to your song is top tier. It's a feeling that can't be explained or duplicated.

Anyway, I ended up taking Lindsay and two of my home-girls from LA, who were in town to the club with me that night. As usual, we had my section turnt the fuck up because we were so lit and so fine. When the DJ finally played my song, me and my girls went crazy. We were so hype that it caused our whole table to turn up with us and we had the whole club lit as fuck, vibing to *"Racthet Pussy"*. It was prob-ably the first moment I had in a very long time where I just felt genuine happiness. Something that I had worked so hard for and damn near begged other people to help me accom-plish had finally come to life and I made it happen on my own. It was my first lesson in not waiting for doors to open. Doing things your way may take a little longer to accom-plish, but in the end, it'll all be worth it. The way that I was proud of myself that night was in a way that I had never felt before.

Once the song finished playing and the DJ gave me a shout out, me and my girls took a shot. We were just about done with our bottles when the bottle girls came to our table with sparklers lit and a sign that read "CONGRATULA-TIONS". They waved the sign around until the sparklers went out and then popped two bottles of champagne. We didn't order any champagne and I usually only got two bottles when I hosted clubs, so I was a little confused where the bottles came from.

"Ay, who ordered these?" I yelled to the bottle girl over the music.

"Oh, it's from Table 4. They wanted to tell you congratulations on your new single." She replied as she pointed at a table full of niggas and about three bitches.

I didn't know anybody at their table but there was a skinny brown skin man with curly hair and bug shaped eyes staring at me. When we locked eyes, he motioned for me to walk over to his table. He should've known better than to think I was ever about to walk my fine ass to another table. Luckily, he got the hint fast and walked over to me instead.

"What's good? I'm Daniel." He said once he finally got over to my table.

"Winter. Thanks for the bottles." I said while I barely even made eye contact with him.

"Oh that ain't shit." Daniel said.

He continued, "You fine as fuck though. Take my number down."

Truth be told, Daniel wasn't really my type. It was nice of him to send us some bottles, but from looking at him, I knew he had to either be a drug dealer or a scammer and I wasn't interested in either. I had never dealt with a drug dealer or a scammer, but I dealt with Cinco who was on that pimping shit and we all remember how that ended. I wasn't willing to deal with people who would do whatever to make ends meet because I learned my lessons about that the hard way.

Despite everything I just said, I still gave Daniel my number after remembering how my girls would talk about the trickin' drug dealers did for them. I could at least get a couple bags out the nigga right?

FOR ABOUT SIX MONTHS, Daniel and I spent time getting to know each other. I felt like I had learned everything there was to know about him. I wasn't ready to take anybody serious or share too much of myself though, so I held back a lot. Plus, I ended up being right about him being a drug dealer and he wanted to spend every fucking second with me. Drug dealers always want their girls to be with them twenty four-seven and that shit doesn't work for me because I'm not no ride-around ass bitch. Like, get you a bitch that don't have motion if that's what you want. Needless to say, I kept dealing with him even though I didn't like that he wanted so much of my time. We would go on shopping sprees, nice ass dinners, pop bottles at the club every week – it was fun, I guess. He was cool to be around when he wasn't getting on my last nerve.

One night he told me to meet him at the strip club when I finished my studio session. Lindsay went to the studio with me that night, so she ended up going with me to the strip club. Daniel never minded if I brought my friends out with us because he was always willing to do whatever to make me happy. When we got to the club, Lindsay and I were sitting next to each other looking at the food menu because if you know anything about Atlanta strip clubs, you know the food is always good as fuck. Daniel and his friends were on the other side of the table ordering bottles when one of the bottle girls came up to me and introduced herself.

"Hey girl, I'm Ashley. Let me know whatever you need tonight and I'll make sure you're good." She said.

"Ok. Cool. Thank you!" I replied.

"Yeah, no problem. I follow you on like every social media platform. I love that you're so nice in person. Most of the influencers and celebrities that come in here are rude as fuck." She kept going.

I don't ever have a problem when people that follow me come talk to me, as long as they aren't being rude or disrespectful, so I didn't mind that she was trying to make conversation with me.

"Aw, thank you!" I said with a smile.

Then she said, "Of course. Do you need any ones for tonight? Or?"

I looked over at Daniel and yelled, "Babe! Did you already get ones?"

He let me know that I could go ahead and get them.

And that's when the bottle girl was like, "Oh. Are you dating Daniel? How is he doing? I haven't seen him since everything happened with his cancer and stuff. It's been months!"

She seemed genuine in her question but I was beyond confused when she brought up him having cancer. After all the time we had spent together and everything he told me about himself from his daughter to where he grew up, he never once mentioned being sick. Obviously I wasn't going to let a bottle girl in a strip club know that she was the one that broke the news to me, so I just played it cool.

"Oh, he's doing good." I said before I started ordering me and Lindsay's food.

I was thinking about that shit the entire night. We were having fun and shit but I kept watching Daniel to see if he appeared to be sick in any way. I didn't want to bring the conversation up at the strip club but I was definitely going to bring it up to him because I needed to know. I'm not going to lie, I was a little irritated because I couldn't understand how he could go six months without telling me that he had fucking cancer. I mean it wouldn't have made much of a difference in anyway, but it just would have been nice to know that the nigga I was dealing with was sick, you know?

After the night was over, Daniel wanted me to go to his house with him but at that point, I told him that I was going to go home since I had Lindsay with me. I could tell that he was irritated but I didn't care. We were months in, but I hadn't even had sex with him yet and quite frankly, I was trying to keep putting it off for as long as I could.

Anyway, the next morning the first thing I did when I woke up was call him and ask about the whole cancer thing. Turns out, the bottle girl was telling the truth. Apparently, Daniel had some kind of knee cancer and won a three million dollar lawsuit because some doctor in Atlanta misdiagnosed him at first. That means, on top of drug money, he had multi-million dollar lawsuit money, too.

I was definitely thrown back by the fact that he didn't tell me about the cancer thing, but I didn't really press him about it because Daniel was a sweet guy. He had a good heart and he always had pure intentions. On top of that, I know he really fucked with me because even though I hadn't had sex with him yet, he still wanted to invest in me and be around me all the time. I think he just liked having a bad bitch on his arm and used me to brag a little bit. So much so that he offered to get me a storefront for *Frost* because he loved how hard I worked for it and how quickly it was growing. He also really believed in my talent and thought that I had the potential to be a star.

The other reason I knew he really fucked with me was because one time I *FaceTimed* him and I could tell he was at *Ikea* because of how the background looked. Everything would have been fine if I didn't hear a bitch talking in the background sounding like she was right next to him. When I questioned whose voice I heard, he rushed me off the phone so my crazy ass pulled up to the *Ikea* and caused a muthafuckin' scene because he shouldn't have tried to play in my face like that. You would think he would have stopped fucking with me after that, but he didn't. Somehow, I think it made him like me even more.

With that being said, about a month after finding out that he beat cancer, I woke up to a text from Daniel telling me to come outside. When I walked out, there was a brand new *Maserati* with a red bow parked in front of my apartment building. Daniel was leaned up against the car with his arms folded across his chest with a smile of accomplishment on his face. He was so excited to see my reaction that I knew the car was mine. I was happy as fuck. Obviously. Who wouldn't be? I screamed and jumped up and down and ran to hug him. See, I didn't tell you this, but, my *Audi* broke down and instead of spending money on a new car, I had just gotten a little *Kia* so that I could get around when I needed to. It was cute but you know I don't do regular anything. My plan was to save up enough money to get the car I really wanted. Daniel knew that I didn't love driving the *Kia* around so giving me the *Maserati* meant so much to me because it showed me how much he really cared about my happiness and listened to the things I said.

Of course, I finally had to give up some pussy after that and of course he reminded me exactly why niggas don't deserve shit. While we were fucking, I was happy to discover that Daniel had a big ass dick, but that didn't matter for too long because about half way into fucking I realized he took the condom off without my permission. Now, at first, I thought maybe I was trippin, so I stopped him and checked for myself. Sure enough, no condom.

"Fuck. Where did the condom go?" I was low key kind of panicking.

"Oh. I took that shit off. I wanted to feel you." Daniel said as if that shit was just okay.

My mind immediately started to race. I was thinking of all of the worst possible scenarios. I knew that I had just come out of a relationship with a man who was on the DL. I knew that HIV/AIDS and STD rates were high in Atlanta, and I knew that I wasn't trying to be nobody's second baby mama. Shit, I wasn't trying to be nobody's first baby mama either. My life was finally going exactly how I wanted it to go and getting pregnant by a drug dealer was not a part of that vision.

I was furious that he had taken the condom off, but I kept my cool and just pretended that the initial shock of not feeling it was what turned me off. Daniel tried his best to get me back in the mood but that shit was a wrap. I didn't even want to be around him at that point so I went to the bathroom to take a quick shower and by the time I got out, I couldn't hold back my anger. As soon as I got out of the bathroom, I went the fuck off on him. I told him that he was a piece of shit for taking the condom off without asking me. In my mind, that gives rapist vibes and I was disgusted. I went off on him for about ten minutes without letting him get a word in and then I grabbed my shit and went home. Mind you I was driving the *Maserati* he got me. But I don't give a damn because buying me a car does not give you permission to take a fucking condom off without telling me. Period.

The morning after, I drove back to his house and forced him to go to the clinic with me bright and early to get tested. I knew it was too early for any STD tests to show up positive, but I was so nervous that I wanted to get tested anyway. I must have gone off on him at least ten times that morning on the way to the clinic. His biggest thing was that he knew he was free of any STD's or anything else he could have given me because he was having his blood tested on a regular basis to make sure his cancer didn't come back. I didn't give a fuck about any of that. Obviously all of our tests came back negative but I was still pissed off because I felt violated and disgusted.

After I took him back to his house, I didn't talk to him for a whole ass month. I was still driving the *Maserati* around, of course, but I was not fucking with him at all. I didn't care how many times he called me, how many times he had his seven year old daughter call me, or how many flower bouquets he had delivered to my house. I wasn't having it. I even went back to the clinic about a week later to get tested again just to make sure my results were still negative. And I mean, they were but I was annoyed that Daniel would even put me in a position to have to worry about it.

To me, the whole situation was a violation of my body and my trust. I bet a broke bitch would have loved the idea of getting pregnant by a nigga that had money but I've been getting my own money my whole life so that wasn't some sort of meal ticket for me. I wasn't even sure I wanted to be with Daniel for real. Him having cancer was some shit that I wasn't sure I was really able to ride out because I didn't know what it really meant. Like, if it came back, how sick would he get? How much pain would he be in? How much longer would he have to live? Those were all questions that ran through my mind and I didn't have the answers to any of them. What I knew for sure though, was that I wasn't prepared to be the strength he would have needed. Not for him or his daughter, so how would I have been that strength for myself and my unborn child? The bottom line is that Daniel was a selfish asshole for taking that condom off and I was having a hard time forgiving him for it.

I'm talking all that shit but eventually, Daniel and I made up. I was basically tired of him begging and having his daughter, who I had never even met, beg for him, too. Things were starting to go back to normal until I was at my house making some guacamole for Lindsay and I and the smell of the ingredients were so nasty I wanted to throw up. I've made guacamole so many times in my life that wanting to throw up before I even ate it was weird and had never happened before. I was confused until Lindsay jokingly hinted at me being pregnant, so I ended up taking a pregnancy test just in case. I was so stuck on getting an STD or

HIV that I forgot that I could've caught the pregnancy disease.

You know I rushed to the store to grab a test and then waited the longest three minutes of my life after I peed on the stick. The idea of being pregnant damn near had my life flashing before my eyes because I knew I wasn't ready to be anyones mama besides Orien. Low and behold, when the time was up, I was fucking pregnant and pissed. I didn't even cry or feel bad or anything. I only felt anger. The first thing I did before I even walked out of the bathroom was *FaceTime* Daniel's stupid ass.

Yet again, I went off on him. I mean, I cussed him smooth the fuck out when that test came back positive. The issue was that he was happy. Not regular happiness either. He was over the fucking moon. To be honest, I had never seen him so happy in all of the time I had known him. But that happiness didn't mean shit to me. As a matter of fact, all it did was piss me off even more.

He was talking about some, "This is exactly what I wanted!"

I'm like, "Nigga. What? Bitch, are you dumb? Nobody has time for a fucking baby!"

There was no way in hell I was keeping that baby so I told Daniel that he needed to give me money for an abortion. I knew he had the money, but he refused to give it to me because he wanted me to keep the baby. He wanted to be a family. But you know me. As soon as my mind is made up about something, that's it. So, instead of waiting for Daniel to get his shit together and give me the money, I knew I was going to have to come out of my own pocket to end the pregnancy but I didn't care. That shit was getting done one way or another.

It was different from the time I was carrying Xavier's child. I was in love with Xavier. I wanted to keep that baby because it was made with love and would have been raised surrounded by nothing but love. With Daniel on the other hand, I wasn't anywhere close to being in love with him and I for damn sure wasn't trying to have his baby, which is why I never would have allowed him to fuck me without a condom in the first place.

GETTING RID of Daniel's baby was not a walk in the park. The universe made sure she gave me hell for it. The first clinic I went to was talking about some "Think about Jesus Christ before you make your final decision." Like bitch, ain't nobody thinking about Jesus fucking Christ. They were on some other shit, so you better believe I got the hell up out of there. That same day, I went to another clinic where I was able to get a same day appointment but there was a five hour wait. At first, it was like *what's five hours compared to eighteen years?* So I was going to wait. But then, there were other girls in the lobby waiting for their appointments and they recognized me from the show. I told you that I don't mind when people recognize me but I was not about to be all over the fucking blogs for sitting in a damn clinic lobby. I don't give a damn what procedure they thought I was getting. That shit was too risky, so I left.

The only person that knew I was pregnant was Lindsay, so I called her on my way back home and told her everything. She suggested a few places for me to call so I hung up with her and the first clinic I called happened to have an appointment for the next day. The only issue was that they only did the abortions that required the patient to be awake and that's not what I wanted. I wasn't trying to be awake while they stuck a vacuum up my coochie – absolutely not. But I was so nauseous and it felt like an alien had invaded my body so I was like fuck it, I'll stay awake if it means they will get this thing out of me.

Lindsay offered to go with me which was perfect because I wasn't allowed to drive myself home after the procedure. I was a little nervous. Not because I was having second thoughts about it but because it was going to be weird being awake while they did it. After filling out all of the paperwork, I ended up asking if Lindsay could go into the room with me and they let her. She sat right next to me, held my hand and watched the doctors vacuum alien guts out of my body while I closed my eyes and prayed for it to be over.

When it was all said and done, Lindsay drove us back to my place and hung out on the couch just in case I needed anything. I got in my bed and just cried for about an hour. For the second time, I ended a pregnancy against my will. Granted, I didn't want to have a child with Daniel, but I also never would have had to have an abortion if he wouldn't have taken that condom off. So yes, two abortions against my will.

It took me about a week to recover mentally, emotionally, and physically from the procedure and I chose to ignore Daniel that whole time because fuck him. When I finally decided to speak to him, I told him what I had done and he was pissed. He was so angry that he had the *Maserati* repossessed. He was corny for that shit, too, but whatever. Even after being a cornball and having my car taken away from me, he still had the audacity to have his daughter calling my phone. For some reason, he thought that she would be able to convince me to take her corny ass daddy back. But for me, it was fuck him, fuck the car, and fuck them kids. Daniel didn't deserve me and I made sure that I completely denied his access to me. He was the fucking poster boy for that saying, "if you corny, you corny – money won't un-corn you."

Even after taking the *Maserati* and every failed attempt to get me back, Daniel was still blowing my phone up on some weird shit. I literally had to block him on all of my social media platforms, block all of his phone numbers and block his daughters number too. Unfortunately, none of that stopped him from calling me, so eventually, I had to change my number because he was too fucking crazy.

6

DEAD & GONE

AFTER DANIEL and I ended our little situation, I decided that I needed to take a break from dating. The shit was draining then and it's draining now – zero out of ten, do not recommend. Sometimes I wish I could actually talk directly to God or the Universe so that I can ask whether or not the niggas that were sent are actually going to start acting right. These men are still out here acting like little ass boys with no communication skills and no self-control. Like, how hard could it be?

Anyway, for the next few months, I just focused on myself, *Frost*, my music, and getting money. I still didn't have too many friends in Atlanta. I was starting to make new connections which was cool but it wasn't like a priority for me or anything. Lindsay and I started spending a lot more time together though, so that was cool. As a matter of fact, when it was time for her to move out of her apartment, my lease was ending too so we ended up moving into a penthouse together. I want to say that Lindsay was the first person that lived with me that wasn't on no type of bullshit. We partied together, chilled in the living room, and watched random shows together. She would pull up to the studio with me from time to time and we just clicked. Remember, she was also a stripper, so I never had to worry about her half of the rent. It felt good to finally have a friend with her own shit. Even though she started off as just a model for my store, she became a really good friend.

Around this time, things were going good for me. Of course I was still working hard to stay out of the dark space I had come from mentally, but I was definitely in a much better space than before. When it comes to shit like your mental health, you have to take it one day at a time. Shit, sometimes you have to take it one hour at a time but either way, you have to acknowledge and celebrate the moments that you made it through, no matter how small they are.

I'll say it had been a good four months since Daniel and I had spoken, Eric and I were still on good terms so we would check in on each other every so often, Kevin and I had smoothed things over via text message, so there was no bad blood there and I hadn't heard from Xavier. As far as I was concerned, my life couldn't have gotten much better than it was. You know the vibe–every time shit is going good for me, something weird happens. So here we go again.

One day I woke up early and decided to do some inventory shopping for my store when I got a call from a number I didn't recognize. Usually I wouldn't answer the phone if I don't know who's calling but the area code looked familiar.

"Hello?" I answered.

The voice on the other end of the phone was like, "Yo. Is this Winter?"

That type of shit irritates me because you know who the fuck you called so why are you asking?

Being that it was so early in the morning, I figured someone must have been playing childish ass games. Let's not forget that when I was fucking with Jail Bae, his little bitch called my phone on some weak shit, too. So at that point in time, I figured anything was possible.

"You called my phone. How you don't know who you're calling?" I said defensively.

"Look. Man. My bad. Look, this Butta. I was just.." His tone was remorseful.

"Butta.. Like Cinco's homie Butta?" I interrupted.

"Yeah. Look, I was just calling to tell you that bro ain't make it." Butta said slowly.

My heart dropped into my stomach. Without asking one single question or Butta saying another word, I knew exactly what he meant. Cinco had died. I'm sure I had lots of questions but I was so shocked that I didn't ask a single thing.

My feelings were all over the place. All I could do was thank Butta for letting me know. When I hung up the phone, I had hella messages from people asking me if I was ok. I was still in a daze after talking to Butta but then I got another phone call and that was when I found out how Cinco had died. He was in a hotel room with some girl named Priscilla, which he had actually cheated on me with before, and he overdosed. Instead of calling 9-1-1, she left him there to die. Part of me didn't give a fuck because of all the shit Cinco had put me through. But the other part of me felt like my world came crashing down around me because of how deeply I loved him when we were together. It was almost like regardless of the fact that Cinco had put his hands on me so many times, him actually dying put a pit in my stomach. My thoughts were all over the place just like my feelings were. To the point where I don't even remember the rest of the conversations I just had. I just remember getting off the phone and going onto social media and seeing so many rest in peace posts for Cinco.

The phone calls I got were confirmation enough for me that Cinco was no longer alive, but seeing so many people post about how much he meant to them and how much they'd miss him, made it even more real than it already was. My thoughts went back to the last time we talked to each other. It was when he was admitting that his laptop didn't actually get stolen but threatening to leak our sex tape was the only way he could grow the balls to tell me that he missed me. Remember that? That memory triggered all of the memories of abuse at his hands that I had and it pissed me off.

For a second, I cried because I was angry with him. I was angry that he had hurt me so badly physically and emotionally. But somehow I was angry with him for dying. And then I started to feel some sense of sadness. Even though we weren't on good terms when he died, we definitely had some really good times when he was alive and I knew that those were the memories I would have to take with me. That doesn't mean I will ever forget the bad shit. It just means that I wanted to remember the good times. The person I fell in love with and the person that Cinco was before he changed into a bad person.

―――――

AT FIRST, I didn't think it'd be appropriate for me to post anything regarding his death but then I remembered that he was a big part of my life and after everything we had been through together, I was entitled to at least a post. Besides that, about a month or two before he died, he had messaged me to see how I was doing, apologize for the way he treated me and to tell me that he would always love me. He told me that he was doing well and had finally stopped sipping lean and he was so happy about that. It's crazy that sipping lean is what ended up killing him. When he died, he had a girlfriend and I wanted to make sure that I mentioned her and was respectful of their relationship by giving my respects in my post. His girlfriend at the time of his passing just so happened to be a girl he had cheated on me with and we had also had some *Twitter* drama involving him years before but none of that mattered anymore. Why would it? He was gone, it shouldn't have mattered. So you'd think right?

Trying to be respectful was all for nothing because I guess his girlfriend and his baby mama felt some type of way about me posting a photo of him. They tried to do all the internet bully shit and I did my best to ignore it all for a few hours but then it became too much so I ended up deleting the post. It just wasn't a battle I was willing to fight. And it was never my intention to bring any negative energy to the whole situation so I was just like fuck it because whether I posted or not, the fact remained that Cinco would never see it.

The crazy thing is that I didn't even go to the funeral because I didn't want there to be any smoke behind me showing up. A lot of the girlfriend's friends were saying it was on sight if I showed up to the funeral, which was fucking stupid because for one, I know that he would have wanted me there and two, it wasn't like she was his girlfriend for his entire life. Nobody had time to be fighting while people were trying to grieve a lost life, so I didn't even consider going to his funeral after that. I still think it was stupid for anybody to feel a way but shit is what it is. Can't change it now, couldn't have changed it then. Cinco is dead and gone and that's that on that.

I'm not going to lie, it took me a while to bounce back after I found out about him dying. It put a lot of things into perspective for me. It's hard for me to really understand my feelings about him dying because he put my life at risk more than once. How can I feel bad that the man that could have killed me, died his own death? But how can I not feel bad that the man that was my best friend at some point, was gone? You see how hard that is? Something told me not to answer the phone that morning and I should've listened. Not that it would have changed the fact that Cinco died, but it would have changed how I received the information and maybe that would have changed how hard it was for me to navigate through it. I don't know.

Obviously my friends were able to see the backlash that I was getting from Cinco's people when I tried to pay my respects on the internet and they were all sending their love and support my way just to try to make me feel better. My homeboy even ended up inviting me out to the club with him and his boys that night so that I could take my mind off of things and partying has always done just that for me; for the moment anyway. Fast forward to me going to the club and I was lit. Any pain or anger I felt surrounding Cinco's death was drowned in alcohol and secondhand smoke. My homeboy really showed up for me. He was making sure that I had whatever I needed and kept making sure I was good the whole night.

At one point, after making sure I was good, he said, "Yo. You should talk to my boy Mike. He's a good dude and he tryna holla."

"Oh. Which one is he?" I asked.

He discreetly pointed toward Mike, "The tall one right there with the red shirt on. He plays ball for the *Hawks.*"

The timing couldn't have been better. It was very on brand for me to party and then meet a new nigga while I was dealing with heartbreak and after two failed relationships with NFL players, I was open to taking my talents to the NBA.

"Oh. He's cute. Make it happen." I said with confidence.

After that, my homeboy introduced Mike and I and of course, we clicked instantly. The common denominator in me instantly clicking with damn near every man I meet is me. Therefore, it's very clear that I'm the vibe and these niggas are attracted like bees to honey.

Mike and I were laughing and joking about everything the entire night. We even left our table to go dance in the middle of the club as if we couldn't do that right there at the table. We were lit though, and just really enjoying each other's company.

While we were dancing, Mike said, "I fuck with you. You should come to Mexico with me tomorrow."

Naturally I laughed because I thought he was just being funny.

"Nah. I'm dead ass. You can bring a friend if you want to. I just want to spend more time with you and I'm 'bout to leave here and hop on a flight." Mike was clearly very serious.

I looked at him for a second just to see if he would say he was kidding. When he didn't, I said, "Alright. Bet. Fuck it. Book the ticket. Let me see if my homegirl wants to come with me."

We danced in the middle of the club for another ten minutes while I texted Lindsay to see if she wanted to go to Mexico. Unfortunately, she didn't have her passport, so she wasn't able to but suggested that I still go because she felt like I deserved it. At first, I was hesitant because I had literally just met Mike, but Lindsay made a good point when she told me that my homeboy wouldn't have introduced us to each other if Mike was a weirdo. That, mixed with everything that happened after I found out Cinco died, made me feel just fine about going to Mexico with a man I just met. Lindsay was right, I definitely deserved it.

Just like that, Mike had my ticket booked and my itinerary emailed to me before the night was over. His flight was before mine, so we exchanged numbers and he told me that he'd pick me up from the airport as soon as I got to Mexico. For whatever reason, I didn't ask any questions or have any real concerns, I was just ready for whatever joy the trip would bring me. What was the worst that could happen? If I got there and hated it, it wasn't like I couldn't book myself an earlier flight home or get a different villa or something. So, after the club, I got home and packed as quickly as I could. It wasn't too much of a struggle because it was Mexico – all I needed was bathing suits, really.

AS PROMISED, when I got to Mexico, Mike was waiting for me at the airport. He had his cousin with him, which didn't bother me at all because I figured I was probably invited to a friend's trip or something. I just assumed that Mike didn't want to travel around Mexico on his own considering he was in another country but also the fact that he was a professional athlete. Whatever the case, the cousin was nice to me and Mike seemed really happy to see me, so I was looking forward to my little vacay in Mexico.

When we made it to our resort, I immediately changed into a bathing suit while Mike and his cousin ordered drinks for us. It seemed like we were just going to play the trip by ear because neither Mike nor his cousin mentioned any solidified plans. I was fine with that because all I wanted to do was drink, tan and relax anyway.

When Mike got back to the room with our drinks, his cousin wasn't with him.

"You ready?" He asked as he handed me a drink.

"Yup. We going to the pool?" I asked.

"Yeah. Well, my aunt wants us to come to see her first, so we'll probably chill with them for a minute to have dinner and drinks." Mike said as he walked toward the door.

That was when I started to get a little confused. Because, aunt? Huh? Like, first I met his cousin and then I was getting ready to meet up with his aunt? It literally didn't make any sense to me. I was downing my drink and thinking *aunt? Why is your aunt here? Is she hot, young, fun, a bad bitch? I don't get it.* But again, I didn't ask any questions, I just went with the flow.

Sure enough, I walked right into a lion's den of this man's entire fucking family. His aunts, uncles, more cousins and his fucking mama. I was literally in shock and a little uncomfortable. But they were all so happy to see him and everybody but his mom was happy to see me as if they had known me for years. I'm not going to lie, the whole situation was very strange but that's what I get for hopping on a flight less than twenty-four hours after I met a nigga.

To make things even more strange, his mom, who like I said, had already made it very clear she wasn't fucking with me, started interrogating me as soon as I sat down.

"So what do you do?" She asked, clearly uninterested.

I'm like, "Oh, I do music and I have an online clothing store."

Mike's cousin overheard and chimed in, "That's crazy! I'm about to start doing music, too. My rap name is going to be Winter."

Me, being the hilarious bitch that I am and trying to ease the tension Mike's mama was obviously feeling, replied with, "Oh, well my rap name is already Winter." I laughed.

My attempt to be funny went way over Mike's mom's head but the cousin laughed a little–even if he was just being nice. In my mind I'm like, *hardy-har, bitch, laugh. Fuck.* But the mom was so uptight and rude that I didn't even know if she was capable of laughing.

She gave me a side eye and said, "Oh, that doesn't matter. He'll be bigger than you could ever be."

I'm thinking like *ok, bitch, this nigga ain't even made a song*

yet, shit, he ain't even introduced himself as Winter yet, like why
the fuck are you so pressed?

Clearly Miss Mama didn't know that I was already lit and very much so that girl but all I said was, "Well, I was just joking, but that's cool, too."

I respectfully walked away after that because I didn't want to have to tell that man's mama off on my first day meeting her.

LATER THAT NIGHT, after she had a few drinks, she made her way over to where I was sitting. I was thinking that maybe she wanted to start over. You know, tell me that we got off on the wrong foot or some shit but no, not even close.

"So what are you trying to do? Are you trying to have a baby with my son? Is that why you're here?" She slurred her words.

What I wanted to say was, "No, you dumb bitch. I just met that nigga so why the fuck would I be trying to have his baby?!"

But what I actually said was, "No, he actually invited me here so I just came to spend a little time with him. That's it. Nothing more. Nothing less."

I was annoyed. Like, bitch, your thirsty ass son met me last night and flew me out why are you asking me all of these fucking questions – I don't even know this nigga for real.

The real struggle was that I was fully prepared to be on a hoe trip. Every single bathing suit I packed was ass out with nothing but my nipples covered and all of my outfits were see through or super short. Imagine how fucking awkward that was for me since we were with his family. Like, what? I mean, it was fine because I was going to do me and be myself regardless and I didn't give a damn who had an issue with it, but like he could have at least given me a heads up or something. Needless to say, I didn't get no kind of dick on that trip and I most definitely cut him off as soon as we touched down in Atlanta because why would you have me on a family vacation when I just met you?!

7

RED FLAGS

AT THIS POINT, it's no secret that I ignore red flags. But it's like every single time I went through some bullshit with a man, another one would come along and make a bitch feel better. I'm not saying it was ever the right thing to do but it's what I did. It usually kept my mind free of my negative thoughts and that's what I always needed the most. It's not like I was ever looking for these men, they would always find me while I was doing my own thing, trying to figure out how to live my best life.

It should have been an automatic red flag that somebody was trying to take me out the country after knowing me for less than twenty-four hours, but of course I try to give niggas the benefit of the doubt. I guess you can call me a hopeless romantic because I really do treat my relationships like cheesy romcom movies, a ghetto romcom, if you will. But after the shit Mike pulled in Mexico, I promised myself that I would stop ignoring red flags. As a matter of fact, after Mexico, I was recording my first album, 'Closure', so I was super locked in the studio. I was also traveling and hosting way more too. I was doing good for about three months until

I came across this *Instagram* page of some fine ass nigga named Shawn.

From what I could tell, he played basketball. Definitely not a super known player but an athlete nonetheless. From the looks of it, he had a unique taste in fashion and a sense of humor similar to my own. Saying Shawn was fine was an understatement, at least to me it was. When I looked through his pictures for the first time I saw someone different than anyone I had seen before; 1 was instantly drawn to him. Looking back I should have exited that page and never EVER looked back. But of course in true Winter fashion I'm always in some shit.

Naturally, the next step was to *Google* him. I had to see what was really going on. I didn't find a girlfriend, no signs of any kids, he had a pretty small contract – under two million dollars – definitely smaller than my exes but he was cute so fuck the money.

After I looked him up and looked at a few more of his posts, I watched his stories and one of them had something to do with the *Girl Scout Thin Mint* cookies and I love those so I figured it was a sign to shoot my shot. No bullshit, it took me like twenty minutes to finally decide that I was just going to send a message and of course when I finally did, he responded immediately. Typical. Part of me hesitated when he responded so quickly because even though I shot my shot first, I knew that I shouldn't have been trying to start anything new while being so locked in with my music and my money. All of that shit went right out the window when I looked at his page again and saw how fine he was –I mean, what's the worst that could happen?

We only went back and forth about the cookies for a few messages and then the conversation just flowed the whole night -- from the DMs, to the texts, to *FaceTime* all in one night. We just clicked instantly. There were never any awkward pauses or silent moments between us, just good conversation and good jokes. We talked every single day for a couple of weeks, so when Shawn finally told me that he wanted me to go to Detroit so that we could meet in person there was no hesitation for me to say yes. In just two weeks of *FaceTime* calls and texting, I knew that I was going to fall in love with Shawn. No lie, within that first week of talking to him, I knew that it was going to be something real. I hadn't felt that kind of natural connection since Xavier.

The entire flight from Atlanta to Detroit had me on edge. I was so nervous. To this day, whenever I hop on a flight to go anywhere, whether it be for hosting, vacationing, or to see a nigga, in the back of my mind I always just think, *I can book an earlier flight home if I need to.* But with this situation, it was different. Like I said, I knew that it could be something real, so I wanted the trip to be special but I knew that there was a fifty-fifty chance that it could just be a failed mission. Whatever the case, when I landed, I went to the bathroom to get myself together before I walked out of the airport to find Shawn. Lindsay knew that I was flying there to see him, so I called her right quick just to take my mind off of how nervous I was. It helped a little because we just talked about random stuff.

When I walked out of the airport, it was snowing outside and Shawn literally pulled up at the exact same time in a bright ass yellow *Jeep*. I can remember the day so vividly – down to the way it smelled outside. Shawn got out of the car and walked around to the passenger side with a big ass smile on his face and my heart pretty much jumped out of my chest because he was taller and finer than what I had been seeing on *FaceTime*. As far as I could tell, he was literally everything I wanted in a man. I was nervous about our first time meeting being awkward but it wasn't, not even a little bit. On the drive to his place, the jokes were there, the conversation was there, and for the first time in a long time I felt like I could be my full self – like I was home in a sense.

SHAWN LIVED in a two-story apartment where his bedroom, living room, and kitchen were on the first floor and guest bedroom and loft were on the second floor. We hung out on the second floor in the loft area where he sat on a beanbag chair and I sat on the couch across from him. We were just chilling, drinking wine, cracking jokes and talking about books we've read. Which, by the way, if you needed another sign that he was my whole ass soulmate, here it is: he actually liked to read like me. I mean I was shocked considering the last man I had dated was a whole country ass drug dealer. Anyway, the longer I sat on that couch and listened to him talk, laughed with him, and bonded with him, the more I wanted him.

Literally like two hours went by without Shawn trying to make a move. I'm thinking like damn, we aren't even next to each other – we were sitting across from each other. So eventually, I walked over to him, straddled his lap while he sat on the beanbag chair and made the first move. And I know you're probably thinking that I made it too easy for him, or gave it to him too soon, but you're wrong because the way that we connected with each other was different than the average connection.

It didn't take long before Shawn picked me up and carried me downstairs to his bedroom. And girl, we were really trying to take each other's soul. I'm convinced to this day that his dick went in and literally hit my heart and a crazy bitch button all at once. I am not lying. You couldn't have convinced me that he wasn't the love of my life. Shit, even I was surprised. There was nothing in the world that could force me to believe anything differently. If you ain't ever had dick so good that you think you're going to marry the nigga based off that alone, you fucking with the wrong niggas.

Anyways, later that night, once we fell asleep – mind you, it was the best after-dick sleep I've ever had, I woke up in the middle of the night to the sound of Shawn's voice. At first, I thought maybe he was on the phone or something, so I didn't say anything and I didn't move, I just listened. But as I listened, I realized he wasn't on the phone. He was actually talking to me while I was sleeping. Well, while he thought I was sleeping.

He said, "I'm here now. You're safe. You don't have to worry anymore."

Obviously I didn't let him know that I heard him because who was I to interrupt his conversation. Besides, he was right. He was there, I did feel safe, and I didn't have to worry anymore. I mean, I can admit that looking back on that now, it sounds a little creepy, like some hypnotizing type shit on the low, but it didn't feel that way at the time. It felt like I had finally met the one.

———

THE NEXT MORNING, Shawn woke up before me and got ready to go to practice. Before he left, he told me that we'd have dinner later that night, let me know that he had left a key on the kitchen counter for me in case I needed to leave for any reason and told me to make myself at home while he was gone. Bitch, I was damn near in love, ok?! By the time he left, it only took me like ten minutes to get dressed so that I could take a walk. Now, Shawn played for Detroit, but he didn't actually live right in the city of Detroit, he lived in a suburb nearby, but it was beautiful. Way different from LA but similar to Atlanta.

As soon as I opened his front door, the trees and their leaves looked like they belonged on a postcard, that's how beautiful they were. Either that or I was already head over heels in love because you know you see things completely differently when you're in love; everything is love and light and shit. Anyway, it was so beautiful that I took a picture of it and posted it on my *Instagram* stories. Because that's what we do when we see something that looks artsy, right? I didn't think anything of it because there wasn't anything that would have identified that I was at Shawn's house or where I was at all.

Even without so much as a street sign in the picture, the internet did what the internet does and within five minutes, blogs started posting my photo with their peanut gallery speculations. It made no sense whatsoever to me that the blogs were able to put two and two together. While the blogs were posting their stories, I started reading comments and there were so many girls commenting talking about who else Shawn was dealing with and how I would be gone shortly.

The stuff about other bitches didn't bother me because in my head I was like, this my nigga now and they would have to physically take him from me before I was coming up off him. But when I went to Shawn's page and saw that he had unfollowed me, I was pissed. Like, that nigga was supposed to be at practice, why the fuck was he on his phone in the first place? But more importantly, why the fuck would he unfollow me in the middle of social media chaos? I was livid.

The only person that knew where I was, was Lindsay, but she wasn't even one of the people hitting me up to see what the tea was. I didn't even care to explain myself to anybody anyway. This shit really wasn't a big deal to me until Shawn unfollowed me. I continued on with my walk, enjoyed the fresh air and the snow and then went back to the house to wait for Shawn to get home.

When he walked in the door from practice, I was sitting upstairs on the couch.

As soon as he walked upstairs I said, "Sit down." With a serious tone.

And his ass sat right down.

"Why would you unfollow me?" I pressed him.

He confidently said, "Because why would you post pictures for blogs to post? I just didn't want to deal with that."

I was so confused because he was dead ass serious. "Shawn. I posted a picture of some fucking snow and some trees. What did I give blogs to post? I didn't know bitches knew what the entire perimeter of your house looked like."

Shawn laughed a little bit.

"Nah, for real. Like that shit made me look so dumb. And on top of that, you could have just let them speculate whatever the fuck they wanted to. You unfollowing me makes it obvious that they were right." I said.

I didn't even give Shawn a chance to reply before I continued, "You need to follow me back right now. I'm not about to look stupid over you." I crossed my legs and sat back on the couch.

And just like that, right then and there, he followed me back. He acted like he had an attitude but I didn't care about none of that. After that, he took a shower and I continued to read blog comments to see what the girls were saying about me. Most of them were just laughing and talking about how many hoes have posted a picture from that same location. That shit doesn't bother me because what difference does it make if it was before me? Anyway, after Shawn took his shower, we had makeup sex and that was when I realized that we had survived our first fight.

Shawn's body was tired from practice, so we chilled and listened to *Sade* for a little while before it was time for us to go to dinner. At dinner, things had basically gone back to normal. Shawn opened up to me a lot more. He shared a lot about his upbringing and about how he lost his grandmother in a traumatic way. He got emotional when he told me about that situation. It was the first time he had shared something so intimate and personal about himself with me. It was also the first time I had ever seen that from a man. I felt closer to him and despite all of my soulmate talk earlier, that was the moment I felt like we really started building a solid foundation for a strong relationship. But, what do we always say? When it's too good to be true, something always has to go wrong. Except, this time, I thought the thing that went wrong was the whole social media disagreement and I loved that we were able to move past that so quickly.

ON OUR WAY back to Shawn's house after dinner, Lindsay called me. For some stupid reason, when I answered, I put her on speaker phone. Mind you, she was the only one of my friends that knew that I was spending time with Shawn so I knew that she wasn't going to say anything about any other niggas or anything like that but she could have started asking questions about the blog shit and for some reason, I just didn't think about that. The conversation started off normal, though, so it didn't matter.

That is until Lindsay said, "Ok. So what are we doing for your birthday, 'cus we need to start planning now."

"Ugh. I don't know yet. I haven't even had time to think about it. Maybe we should just get a boat and then do a cute dinner after." I said.

"Yeah, that's cute. Shit, just have Shawn pay for everything." Lindsay casually said on fucking speaker phone.

My heart dropped as soon as the words came out of her mouth. I damn near wanted to throw up but I was trying to stay cool.

"Girl. Have who, do what?" I choked.

Lindsay was completely oblivious. "Just have Shawn pay for it. That's your man, so why wouldn't he?"

I started laughing as a way to ease the tension I felt building up in the car.

"No, psycho. I said I was going to meet him." I said.

"Oh shit." Lindsay laughed.

I was relieved. "Yeah, bitch. You're moving too fast. But I don't know what I want to do for sure yet. I'll figure it out by the time I get back." I tried to smooth things over.

"Alright, cool. Well, have fun. Hit me later." Lindsay said.

We hung up the phone after that but I could feel that Shawn had an attitude.

Before I could even say anything, Shawn said, "Why is she saying just have Shawn pay?"

"Well you heard the whole conversation, she misunderstood. She thought you were my man." I said.

"That's weird. I don't like weird shit like that. She talkin' about some just have him pay. Like, that shit is weird." Shawn was obviously irritated.

Naturally, I started to get upset because he was upset. I just didn't feel like it was that big of a deal. It was legitimately just a misunderstanding. And like, girls just talk shit like that all the time. I had no intention of asking him to pay for shit and I wasn't walking around telling people he was my man so I started to get mad because I felt like he was playing in my face. We argued the entire drive home and I can admit that I overreacted because I was embarrassed and got defensive when I felt he was mad at me for something I didn't even say myself. So, when I was finally able to calm down a little, I explained to him that Lindsay was the only person that knew I was talking to him and I hadn't spoken to her any other time the entire trip beyond the conversation he had just heard. It didn't matter that I was calm or that I gave him as much reassurance as I could because Shawn let it be known that I had lost his trust.

I felt like 'losing his trust' was a little aggressive for the situation because again, it literally wasn't that big of a deal. It's not like she was on the internet spreading false information or some shit. She literally thought he was my nigga and then acknowledged her mistake. Like, what the fuck? I don't understand why he was so butt hurt. Plus, it was my last night with him and he was making that shit awkward by being upset over nothing. We should have been having sex and making memories but instead, he was mad at me for something the next bitch said. Luckily, we ended up brushing it off by the time we got back to his house and we were able to chill, listen to music, drink wine and just vibe together.

THE NEXT MORNING, I was dreading leaving Shawn. I was really going to miss him. I was feeling like the trip in a sense was a success but also a fail because we had to navigate through two different negative situations our first time spending time together. You know that type of passion in a relationship can go one of two ways; it could bring us closer or tear us apart and that's what scared me. I didn't want the little shit to tear us apart so soon.

While my *Uber* was on the way to take me to the airport Shawn and I had sex again. The sex between us was off the charts. Truly, I don't think I've even had that type of sexual chemistry with another person since him and that's also what made this relationship so fucking complicated. Everything really was just too good. And despite the fact that we had already had some hard moments I knew he felt the same way I did. I damn near missed my flight trying to get that quickie in but it would have almost been worth it.

Assuming that Shawn felt the same way I did was an accurate assumption, however, since he felt like he couldn't trust me, he ended up telling me that he felt like we should just chill once I got back to Atlanta. Which is why I said it would have *almost* been worth it. Like, how you just fuck me that good, then tell me we gotta chill? That was so weak to me but it was like what was I going to do – beg? No. My feelings were hurt but some part of me felt like he was speaking out of frustration. I don't know why but part of me just felt like he didn't really mean it. I'll never beg a nigga to fuck with me, so I took it for what it was but I didn't feel like it was permanent.

8

DEAL WITH THE DEVIL

ONE THING for certain and two things fa sho, whenever I feel down about a nigga, I level up and get more money. I used my flight from Michigan back to Atlanta to acknowledge the fact that I felt some type of way about the way things ended up between Shawn and I, but I knew I had to shake that shit off. I was genuinely confused as to why he didn't trust me based off of one stupid situation that wasn't even a big deal, but I couldn't harp on it because it wasn't going to make a difference. So, by the time I accepted it for what it was, I pushed the whole situation to the back of my mind as best as I could.

My birthday was only a couple of weeks away, so my main focus was to decide how I was going to celebrate. I've never been big on celebrating my own birthday, I literally cry every year. I just feel like it's so awkward forcing a bunch of people to come together to celebrate you. The only time I've felt loved and really happy on my birthday was on my 21st when Xavier threw me a surprise party. Although I had all these feelings about my birthday I still planned to do something because I knew I'd just feel worse if I didn't.

WHEN I SETTLED in at home, I filled Lindsay in on everything that had happened after we last spoke and she was just as confused as I was about the whole situation. She felt bad because she made an honest mistake but there really wasn't anything to feel bad about – the shit was stupid. Regardless, I was happy to be back home to my own bed, my own shower, and to my main man, Orien.

Later that night, I decided that I'd just do my birthday in LA. I had more friends in LA than I did in Atlanta and I wanted to get in the studio while I was there. Instead of texting everyone I knew to see if they'd be in town, I posted a quick message in my stories that said, *who's gonna be in LA next week*? Sure enough, all my bitches in LA hit me back with the quickness. So right then and there, I knew it would be lit. Soon after, a promoter hit me asking me if I wanted to host while I was in town and you know hosting is always easy money so it was a great way to kick off my birthday weekend.

Lindsay wasn't from LA, but I knew she'd be down to go with me, so I sent her a text telling her to come to my room so that I could invite her.

"We're going to LA for my birthday. Let's go shopping tomorrow." I said as soon as she came into my room.

Lindsay laughed, "That was fast. Ok, I have a shoot tomorrow morning, so let's go to *Lenox* after."

Even though I knew she'd be down, I was excited to hear her say it. "Yay. Ok, cool. I'm going to book my flight right now, so I'll just book yours too."

She walked over and sat on the edge of my bed, "Ok, how long are you staying?" She asked.

"I'm actually probably going to stay like a week because

I'm going to book some studio time too, but I'll book your flight back for whenever." I said.

"Yeah, I definitely can only stay like two days because I have two fittings and another shoot coming up." Lindsay said as she hugged Orien.

Things were already starting to look up. Not that they were really down, but you know a quick little heartbreak can be inconvenient if nothing else. Anyway, I booked our flights and started to tell my girls in LA what the plan was. Since I was going a week before my actual birthday, I just wanted to keep it simple by day-drinking at brunch and then having a fly ass dinner before we went to the club.

The next day, Lindsay and I went to *Lenox Mall* to get a few outfits for our trip and that night, we were on our flight getting lit.

———

DO YOU REMEMBER RONALD? The manager that basically took advantage of my music career after I left that white-girl rap group,*Mob Mentality*. I hadn't seen him in who knows how long because every time I would try, he would come up with an excuse and flake on me. Well, I don't know how he ended up finding out that I was back in LA, but he called me pretty much as soon as I got there.

"Winter. It's Ronald, how you doin', girl?" He said as soon as I answered the phone.

To be honest, I'm not sure why I answered his phone call because Ron had actually made it really hard for me to move forward with my music career. I wrote and recorded so many songs in his studio and he knew that I wanted them, that's why he would always flake on me when I tried to meet with him. So, I guess I was just curious to see what it was that he had to say.

"What's up, Ron." I said, dry as fuck.

He cut right to it.

"I heard you dropped new songs. You sound good. We have a lot of unfinished business, so I wanted to get with you about investing some money into you so that we can get you signed." Ron said with confidence as if he had already invested so much into me.

At that point in time, *'Ratchet Pussy'* was doing well – especially considering it was my first single in years. I did a pretty good job building a fanbase on my own and I was proud of that. I knew that if I had the right team and a real budget behind me, my music career would really take off, so when Ron mentioned investing and getting me signed, I was all in.

"Oh. Ok. That sounds cool. We can definitely talk if you're serious." I said.

I was trying to make sure I didn't sound like I was too thirsty for his support after he fell off of the face of the Earth all those years.

"No, yeah. I'm serious. Just let me know when you have time this week and we'll coordinate." He said.

I wanted to keep the ball in my court because it made me feel like I'd have more of an advantage that way. "Alright, well I have the studio booked for a couple of days this week, so you can just meet me there whenever you have time. I'll send you the info."

Not gonna lie, it also felt like a flex to tell him that I already had a studio booked for a few days since I used to use his studio for free in the past.

"Ok, great! That sounds good." Ron sounded excited.

After that, we talked about irrelevant shit for a few minutes and then we got off the phone. I didn't know how much of an investment Ron wanted to make and I didn't know exactly what he could do to help me get signed, but I was secretly looking forward to meeting with him. I didn't get my hopes up, but I did appreciate the fact that he obviously saw that I was really on my shit. It showed me that my talent really does speak for itself.

———

THE NEXT COUPLE of days were all about me! My girls had gotten me a birthday cake, flowers, balloons, and a bottle. We were all excited to just turn the fuck up and it felt good to be surrounded by so much genuine love. When we were at brunch, there were a few niggas there that kept sending us shots, so we were all super lit. Lindsay fit right in with my girls from LA too, and I loved that. Everything was good until after about ten shots when I started to think about how much I missed Shawn. You know how that shit goes. Luckily I had my friends around me to tell me not to text that nigga. After brunch, we went back to my homegirls house because we all needed a nap to sober up and recharge.

Later that night, we went to *Nobu* for dinner and then had the club going up. The DJ played *Ratchet Pussy* and bottles kept coming to my table all night. It was probably one of the best nights I had in a while. I don't think I gave niggas any type of attention that night either. Like, I was really just out with my girls, celebrating all of my achievements for my birthday and manifesting the success that was to come – very much boss bitch energy.

———

LINDSAY'S FLIGHT was bright and early the next day, so she took an *Uber* to the airport. I really loved our friendship because there was no drama, no pressure, and no judgment. And I'll keep saying this – she paid her rent on time – which automatically made her solid in my book. Anyway, I'm glad that she was able to make her flight on time because I was so hungover that I slept until it was time to get ready for my studio session.

Even though I was hungover, I was ready to get in the booth and go crazy. I loved recording in LA. Plus, I didn't know whether or not Ron was really going to show up, but I was going to make sure that if he did, I blew his fucking mind. It may have been petty of me to do this, but I didn't send him any type of reminder or follow up with him in any type of way to see if he still had plans of pulling up. I just felt like that nigga had flaked on me so many times in the past that I didn't even want to give him the satisfaction of having the chance to do it again.

To my surprise, as my *Uber* pulled up to the studio, Ron was standing in front talking on the phone. It was surprising because I wasn't really expecting him to show up at all, so the fact that he was there on the first day and early at that, showed me that he was serious.

"You're here early." I said as I walked up to him.

"Yeah, I was already on this side of town so I figured I'd just handle a few phone calls while I waited for you." He said as he gave me a hug.

My mind was racing as we walked into the studio because it was just so weird to me that all of a sudden Ron wanted to work with me again. Also because I wanted whatever conversation we were about to have, to be something that made sense for me. I worked hard to build my music career up again and I didn't have time to play games. While those thoughts raced through my mind, neither of us said a word as I checked in and was shown to the studio I was going to be using. I can only assume that his mind was racing just as much as mine was, but who knows.

"How much you paying for each session?" Ron asked as soon as we walked into the studio.

"Oh. I got this shit for the low. I'll end up paying $1500 for all three days." I said.

Ron said, "Ok, I'll handle the rest of it at the front desk before I leave."

I was surprised but not flattered. "Oh, cool. Ok. Thanks." I said.

"So look, your new shit sounds really good…" Ron wasted no time.

"Thanks." I said as I sat down.

Ron didn't even bother sitting down. "I'm ready to put up $50k to get you signed. So videos, studio time, whatever you need, let's get this shit going. It's time."

"Ok. Well, shit, I already have the treatment for *Ratchet Pussy*, I'm ready to shoot a video for that ASAP." I said.

"How soon can you get that done? Or when are you going back to Atlanta?" He asked.

"I can get it done as soon as I go back. I been ready. I'll set everything up tonight and tomorrow and shoot it next week as soon as I get back." On the inside, I was hype but I kept it real G on the outside.

"Yeah, let's do that. I'll see if there's any flights and just meet you out there. So book whatever you need to book and then send me the invoices. He said.

"Bet. You want to hear what I been working on?" I asked.

"Nah. I actually have to get to another meeting, so I'm going to go pay for the rest of your sessions for this week and head out. I'll try to get back here before you leave, if not, I'll catch you in Atlanta." Ron said as he started to make his way toward the door.

I kept it simple. "Alright, cool. Thanks."

And just like that, I had signed another deal with the devil.

Except that time, he didn't even bother to present me with any paperwork and I didn't bother to ask for any. The way I saw it was that paying for the remainder of my studio sessions while I was in LA and covering the cost of the video shoot in Atlanta wasn't even going to cost him much. The return on his investment was going to be way more. I was sure of it.

I was in the studio for the next two days killing every beat I got on. I was so proud of myself because I knew that my hard work was already paying off without Ronald but I knew that it would pay off even faster when he got me signed. I wanted to get the most out of his $50k, and Ron made sure that the video shoot was booked for as little money as possible without taking away from the quality. He was only going to end up coming out of pocket about one thousand dollars for the shoot and I found out later that he was able to finesse the rest of my studio sessions down to just five hundred dollars. He was good at that – being cheap.

WHEN I GOT BACK to Atlanta, everything went smooth for the video shoot. Ronald was really impressed with how I handled business, my work ethic and the concept of the video. As a matter of fact, when we wrapped the shoot, Ron told me that a distribution company called Kingdom Music was going to push my album when it was finished and I was super happy about that. According to him the deal was already locked in. Things were feeling way different with Ron than they had felt before. It actually felt like we were a team and I really believed that he was about to help me blow up.

Over the next couple of months, Ron started handling all of my bookings and we shot videos for 'Made of Glass' and 'Get Around' and each of those videos were shot for only a thousand dollars too. The *'Ratchet Pussy'* video had gotten such good feedback that I was starting to grow a larger fanbase and more producers were reaching out to work with me. Ron and I had meetings with a few different labels and we even had offers on the table but they were low and I knew that I was worth way more than they were offering so we declined them all.

In the meantime, I was in the studio writing and recording. At the time, I didn't really need a producer because I already had a bunch of beats that I hadn't used yet. I was in the studio pouring my heart out on these tracks. Every song that I wrote was personal and therapeutic. Out of twelve songs, most of them were about Xavier and a couple of them were about Shawn. It was my way of finding closure from those situations. It was my way of moving on with my life since I would never get the real closure I needed from them. It only made sense to name the album *'Closure'*.

'Closure' was such a raw and real album that I knew that with or without Kingdom Music or any other label, it was going to do well but knowing that I had a distribution deal with them gave me even more confidence. Yeah, there was some part of me that was nervous for people to listen to it because I was so vulnerable in every song and I had always worked so hard to keep any of my real feelings or emotions off of the internet. But those nerves didn't change the fact that I knew that I was talented and Ronald, Kingdom Music, and every single listener was about to see just how talented I was. Overall, I was excited to be dropping new music and getting back to my first real dream.

AFTER ABOUT A MONTH, when I finally dropped the album, it did even better than I expected. Not only did my fans love it, but I had more producers hitting me up trying to get in the studio with me and a few videographers offering to shoot videos for me. It was lit. I probably didn't show it, but I was so damn proud of myself. After every obstacle that detoured me from music, I had finally gotten a distribution deal and dropped a dope ass project – I was finally walking into the life I was supposed to be living. I was so happy you would have thought my shit went platinum. Ronald was happy too. I mean shit, my album was doing numbers which meant I was making money and that meant that he was going to be able to start earning the return on his initial investments.

Anyway, one producer in particular had actually contacted me directly instead of contacting Ron. And normally, if something like that would happen, I would just ask the producer to reach out to my "manager" aka Ron like I had done with all of the other producers. But this particular producer was trying to fuck with me too which was why he didn't hit management first. Lucky for him, I liked his energy. Typically, I keep a hard line between business and pleasure. On top of that, I had been working so hard and was always so busy that I didn't have time to get a new boo. Honestly, I hadn't given anybody the time of day because even though I hadn't spoken to Shawn much since we ended things, I was still stuck on him. Bad.

Long story short, me and the producer nigga, Toon, started spending time together. He'd invite me to his studio sessions, we'd have sessions together, and we'd go on dates and shit too. It wasn't anything serious but it was just enough to keep my mind from missing Shawn too much and something to do when I wasn't busy.

One night, Toon and I were at my house sitting on the couch, just chillin', watching TV, and then we started talking about my album streams. He asked me who pushed my album and I told him the whole story about Kingdom Music and how Ronald put everything together for me. I low key felt good about it when I was telling him because I loved the fact that I finally had a team.

After I told him the whole story, Toon showed me his phone and said, "Nah, babe. This says that a company called CoD pushed the album."

Without even taking the time to look at the phone, I said, "Oh, yeah, CoD is Ron's company, but the distro company is who pushed it."

And then it dawned on me that I had never seen any paperwork for the distribution deal Ron told me about. We never signed papers for his initial investment and by the time he told me about the distribution deal, we were already super locked in. I trusted Ron because everything was seemingly going well, so I just never even thought to ask about seeing the paperwork for the distribution deal with Kingdom Music.

"Wait..." I said as I grabbed the phone from Toon's hand. "Why would CoD be on there at all?"

As I held his phone in my hand, I stared at Ron's company name, CoD, on the screen. That was the moment that I realized that Ron lied to me. After all of the time that passed, all the hard work that I had put in, I let Ronald play in my face because I just fucking trusted him. There was never a distribution deal. Ron used his company to distribute my album and collect the earnings and I was fucking livid. Truth be told, I was on such a high from the feedback I was getting from the album that I didn't even realize I wasn't cashing any checks. Not only was I not seeing a dime from the streams, but Ronald wasn't even putting up crazy amounts of money for him to be trying to collect shit.

When it became clear that Ronald had played me, I gave Toon his phone back and just sat quietly on the couch. I really couldn't believe it. Some part of me was upset with myself for allowing Ronald to play me again. Some part of me was confused on how and why he thought it was normal to scam somebody the way that he did me.

For the rest of the night I was zoned out. Toon kept telling me not to stress it but he didn't know the history Ron and I had. He didn't know that it wasn't the first time Ron snaked me but it was for damn sure going to be the last. When Toon finally fell asleep, I sat down and wrote out every dime that Ron spent on my career from the moment he offered the fifty thousand dollar investment. The total came out to about eight thousand dollars – nothing close to fifty thousand.

The next morning, Toon left and the first thing I did was call Ron.

I didn't even greet him when he answered the phone. "Why does it say that CoD distributed my album and not the whole ass distribution company we discussed?"

Ron sounded irritated. "Winter."

"No. Winter, nothing. You work for *me* nigga. I don't work for you. So why the fuck are *you* collecting my album money?" I said aggressively. I was pissed.

Ron laughed sarcastically, "Winter. Do you know how much money I've invested in you? I don't think you truly understand how the music industry works. An investment is not free money. You still have to…"

I cut him off. "I still have to *what*? Because you've invested about eight thousand dollars so far. That's about forty-two thousand dollars short of the fifty you claimed you were putting up. Obviously I'm still not signed. So what the *fuck* don't I understand?"

Ron laughing was what really set me off. It felt belittling and disrespectful and I wasn't going for that shit.

"Send me the streams right now. I want to see everything.

You think this shit is a game and it's definitely not that." I said.

"How about we set aside some time for you to come to LA so that we can have a proper meeting?" Ron said.

"Say less. I'll be there this week." I said before hanging up in his face.

His calmness really bothered me. Music meant so much to me and I had put in so much time, energy and effort into my music that it was offensive that Ronald thought he was owed something. Especially since he hadn't actually kept up his end of the deal. Even worse than that, he lied. I didn't want to go to LA to have a fucking proper meeting. I wanted my music to be mine. I wanted to see what I had earned. I wanted to be released from whatever bullshit deal I had made with the devil. Ron and I didn't settle anything that day but as soon as I hung up on him, I booked a flight. One thing a nigga won't play with is my money and I think Ronald's ass thought he was going to get away with his shit by setting up a 'proper meeting'.

9

FRAUD

TWO DAYS LATER, I touched down in LA ready to kick in whatever door I needed to, to make sure that Ronald knew that I wasn't the one to play with. The first thing I did when I landed was send a text that said, *send an addy.* Surprisingly, Ron replied right away with an address and I took an *Uber* straight there from the airport. To be honest, I didn't really have a plan, I just knew that I needed to raise hell about my music the best way I could. I worked too hard and went through too much to allow Ron, or any man for that matter, to steal from me. That's basically what Ron had done – stolen from me. He took advantage of my circumstances when he and I first met and then he attempted to do it again by publishing my music as if he was the one that owned it.

When I got to the address that he gave me, I realized that it was a studio in North Hollywood. I had never been to that particular studio before but I was familiar with it because I knew a few producers that booked sessions there pretty often. Anyway, when I got inside, I asked the front desk receptionist where Ronald's session was and just as she started to look through her computer, Ron came out of one of the rooms.

"I got it, Ashley. Thanks, sweetheart." Ron said to the receptionist.

I didn't even greet him or thank her, I just stormed right past him and into the room he came out of.

There were no other artists, producers or engineers in the room, so I'm not really sure what he was doing there, but it didn't matter because I knew what I was doing there. Ronald slowly closed the door behind him and opened his mouth – I can only assume it was to make small talk, but I didn't have time for that.

"Open your laptop. Show me my streams." I said with a fucked up attitude.

He had a sinister smirk on his face as he walked toward a chair. "Winter. Sweetheart, I can't show you your streams. I have other artists whose music is also in that account and I can't break the confidentiality clause by showing the streams for your music." He said as he sat down.

His nonchalant, condescending tone and demeanor was really pissing me off.

"You work FOR ME! What don't you understand about that?! I don't give a fuck about no other artists or what the fuck their music is doing! I want to see MY shit." I yelled.

Ron interlocked his fingers and placed them in his lap. "I'm sorry, Winter. My hands are tied. You're just going to have to trust me." He said.

"Trust you?! Nigga are you out of your mind? Let me see my fucking streams!" I was louder that time.

He shrugged his shoulders. "No can do."

I was so angry I wanted to cry, beat Ron's ass, and destroy that whole studio all at once. I couldn't let him know he held that type of power over me though. I couldn't give him the satisfaction of knowing he had gotten under my skin the way he did.

"You're a bitch. You're so fucking weak that you have to steal from women and that makes you a disgusting human. You don't have to show me shit. That's cool. We both know I'm the only artist you had, but you just lost me, too. I never needed shit from you and when I'm done with you, you'll wish you never played with me." I said before I stormed out of the studio.

Ronald didn't say a word. He just looked me dead in my eyes as I said what I had to say. He kept that stupid ass smirk on his face the whole time but I know that he knew, that I knew, that he was full of shit.

———

THERE WAS a liquor store next to the studio, so that's where I went while I waited for my *Uber* to pull up. My mind was all over the place and I was fighting to hold back all types of emotions because I knew that I wasn't going to be able to beat Ronald on my own. I wasn't emotional because I was hurt. I was emotional because I was pissed the fuck off. If you've ever been so mad that you cry, then you know mad tears hit way different than sad tears. If it wasn't one thing, it was always another and I was tired of that. Beyond lying and stealing from me, Ronald was about to force me to come out of pocket to get a lawyer just to get back what was already mine.

By the time I bought a water bottle from the liquor store, my *Uber* pulled up. I was so deep in my thoughts that I didn't even greet the driver, I just sent a text to my homegirl Nikki, letting her know that I was on my way to her house. It took about fifteen minutes to get there and the whole time all I could do was replay in my mind how disgustingly nonchalant Ronald was in the studio. It was almost adding fuel to my flame of vengeance. It was causing my anger to turn into determination. The determination to do everything that I could on my own before I needed to resort to a lawyer and the determination to make even more music so that I could show him that he didn't run shit or stop shit.

The first thing I did when I made it to Nikki's house was tell her everything that happened with Ron at the studio. It felt good to get it off my chest and it also felt good to have my friend validating all of the feelings of frustration that I harbored. Once I was done telling her everything, Nikki suggested that I try to reach out to the streaming company directly. She was basically saying that if I reached out directly and explained how much of a fraud Ron was, they might be able to remove any and all of his information from my music, which would give me back ownership and allow me to collect the money I was earning. To me, that sounded logical and since I wanted to do as much as I could without a lawyer first, I was definitely willing to try.

MY FLIGHT back to Atlanta was the next morning. The only reason I had flown to LA was so that I could meet with Ron's dumb ass in person, so after Nikki and I chilled for a little while, I showered. While I was in the shower I told myself that I was going to start researching the streaming company and decide what I wanted my email to say because I figured I was probably going to be up all night anyway. Usually, when my mind is all over the place, or my heart is broken, I can't sleep, but that night, I had no trouble falling right asleep. My mind was so tired that I didn't even attempt to do any research on the streaming company and didn't even consider what my email would say, but I put a short to-do list in my notes so that I could try to get some things done at the airport and on the plane.

On my flight the next morning, frustration was still fueling my determination. Before the flight landed, I had figured out who to contact within the company that was streaming my music and I also put together a very well-written email explaining my situation and offering to send over any proof they would need from me that would help expedite the process. Not only was I confident that it would work, I was also motivated to get in the studio so that I could get more music out – under my ownership.

IT TOOK ABOUT two days before I heard back from the streaming company and when I did, they told me that Ronald had a contract, signed by me, that stated he owned the rights to my music and its publishing. At first, I was a little confused by the email because I knew that I didn't sign any new contracts with Ronald. Hell, he never even pulled out a single sheet of paper when he offered to invest, get me signed or when he claimed I had gotten the distribution deal. I must have read that email ten times before it dawned on me that Ronald could have very well sent them a bullshit contract so I replied to the email requesting that they send me a copy of the contract they had on file and they sent me some bullshit.

Remember, the first and only contract Ron and I had ever signed was way back in the day, five years before, to be exact. It was only a twelve month contract so it would have expired long before Ron ever reached out to me again. That man was evil enough to edit that old ass contract. He used my signature, a copy of my social security card and a copy of an ID I had from high school to create a new contract with current dates and details. I couldn't believe what I was seeing.

Another issue, besides the fact that it was fraud all together, was that his new, bullshit contract didn't even have my name spelled correctly. The only thing authentic about that contract was that my signature really was on the bottom of it, but only because he had stolen it from the old, outdated paperwork.

When I saw all of the discrepancies in the contract, I damn near wanted to cry tears of joy because I knew that it was going to be easy to prove that Ron was obviously a fraud doing very fraudulent things. So, naturally, I went through my email to find the original paperwork from years ago. I wasn't even sure if I'd have a copy because it was so long ago and nothing ever came of the twelve month contract. Lucky for me I found a copy and sent it over to the streaming company proving that he had written up fake paperwork to steal my music. Crazy enough, about an hour later, I got an email from them letting me know that I should seek legal counsel because there was no way for them to determine whether I was telling the truth or if Ron was. Imagine having cold hard evidence and they tell you that a lawyer has to tell them because the obvious proof isn't good enough. I felt defeated.

The frustration that was once fueling determination had started to spark depression. Ronald was a piece of shit for taking advantage of me the way that he did and his actions combined with the fact that I felt somewhat helpless, had the potential to send me into my dark hole again and I couldn't afford that mentally or financially. I didn't even bother replying back to the person that basically told me I needed a lawyer to prove the truth.

At that point, it was fuck whoever they were, fuck Ron, and fuck the album he stole from me. *'Closure'* meant a lot to me, but if I wasn't going to be making any money off of it, then Ron wasn't going to be making money off of it either. I removed any trace of the songs and videos that were on that album from all of my social media platforms and decided that no matter how long it took for me to hire the best lawyers in the game, I would do it. In the meantime, I was just going to have to continue to get money and make more music.

10

LESSON LEARNED

I CAN'T LIE, finding out that Ron played me really hurt. In part because I trusted him but mostly because I allowed him to play in my face again. I'm not one to regret things, but my music was my one true dream and me being too naive had cost me my first real project. Life is funny though, because even though I said fuck the *'Closer'* album, it actually started to do really well. Music was finally starting to take off for me and it was bittersweet because that's what I always wanted. The problem was that I wasn't collecting a dime from it – Ron was. A few months had passed since I saw him and even though I was frustrated that he was collecting money from music he stole from me, I had to stay focused on dropping my new single, *'Obsessed'*, on my own.

Around the same time I was getting ready to drop *'Obsessed'*, Toon and I started spending less time together. It wasn't for any reason other than I just wanted to focus on my shit without any distractions. We weren't serious, there were no heavy emotions involved and it didn't require any type of break up conversation, I just became less available and he didn't press me about it. It was what I felt was the best thing for me to do at the time.

I was probably more focused than I had ever been before and I think that the universe was rewarding me for that because right before I was supposed to release 'Obsessed', someone reached out to me asking if I was available to perform at *Rolling Loud*. I'm not going to lie, at first, I thought Ron was on some bullshit but after a few emails back and forth and then a phone call, I quickly realized that he had nothing to do with it and I was really being booked for *Rolling Loud* — one of the most lit music festivals there is. Obviously I was hella excited to be performing and I wasn't going to allow anything Ron had done prevent me from showing up and showing the fuck out.

This time around, I made sure that I paid very close attention to the paperwork that was sent over to me. If I didn't gain anything else from dealing with Ron, I definitely gained the knowledge to make sure that all of my T's were crossed and my I's were dotted. I didn't have a manager at the time because that was a part of Ron's job and to keep it real, I wasn't sure I could trust anybody to manage me again. I read the contract over and over again as many times as I could to make sure that it really made sense to me. After that, I called a friend of mine and asked him to look over it and when we both felt as though there was no sneak shit written in, I signed my first performance contract. I couldn't believe it but I knew that I deserved it.

Immediately after the contract was signed, I started to put my setlist together and decided that I was going to hire dancers. Of course, I had to come out of my own pocket for that, but it was an investment toward the opportunity of a lifetime. The fact that I was going to be able to perform my own music at an event as big as *Rolling Loud* was really my first testament to what it means when they say 'hard work pays off'. Not only that, but it also felt like a big 'fuck you' to Ronald. Imagine stealing my music from me just to have to watch me perform some new shit on the main stage at *Rolling Loud* and in my hometown at that. Ha. Ya girl was *really* on some fuck that *'Closure'* album after that but I did include one song from the album in my set. Even though I didn't want Ron to earn a dime from my songs, the whole project was doing really well so it only made sense for me to give my fans a live performance of at least one song off the album. I was going to perform *"Get Around"*, *"Doin It"*, *"Say Too Much"* and *"Ratchet Pussy"*.

The closer *Rolling Loud* got, the more I reflected on my life leading up to the moment I was asked to perform. See, when I was part of Mob Mentality, we performed in some pretty dope theaters and had some pretty big shows but I knew that those shows weren't going to be shit compared to a festival – especially *Rolling Loud*. On top of that, when I was with that group, I was performing their songs, not mine. Even then, I felt like the Mob Mentality part of my journey was a stepping stone that prepared me for *Rolling Loud*. With or without them, my talent never wavered and my light was never dim, but touring with Mob Mentality taught me stage presence and the art of working a crowd. I was getting ready to be on stage working the biggest crowd of my life while performing my own shit. Everything was coming full circle for me. The TV show had given me a larger platform than being a stripper or being in a girl group had given me and my tenacity, personality, and talent had given me the ability to grow and maintain that platform. I deserved the opportunity to perform on the main stage at *Rolling Loud*. Better yet, I earned it.

FAST FORWARD TO the day of the show and it was lit! Overall, I wasn't even nervous. I mean, of course I had a few pre-show butterflies because I wanted everything to be perfect but it wasn't anything major. Oh, and there was a small little glitch right before I went on stage because my microphone wasn't working for like ten seconds which obviously made me anxious but it worked itself out real fast. My dancers, my DJ, and my friends were just as excited as I was and I loved that for me. Genuine love and support from people in your corner is really priceless. Plus, my set was literally everything I could have imagined it to be and doing it in *the Bay* at *Rolling Loud* made it even better. Between dancers, hair, makeup, wardrobe, and travel expenses, I definitely spent more money than I made that day, but I knew that I would get it all back once I dropped new music.

After *Rolling Loud*, I was on an emotional high for about a week. I watched footage from anywhere I could find it and took notes on my performance so that I could make sure I was even better the next time I touched a stage. I really loved all of the feedback I was receiving. I loved accomplishing such a huge goal on my own – no label, no manager, no budget, no co-sign, just me. There were so many times that I would find myself saying, *see, I was right*, in my head because even in my darkest days, I knew that I was different. I knew that I was special. I knew that I was a star and I felt like I had finally proven that to myself and anybody who had the audacity to doubt me.

Once my performance confetti settled, I was ready to drop *'Obsessed'*. I knew that it was going to do well, but there were a lot of secret emotions connected to it because it was going to be the first single I dropped after finding out that Ron stole my music. Emotions never stopped me from getting to the bag before and I wasn't going to let them stop me then, but I definitely took a moment to acknowledge them.

Unfortunately, not even a full twenty-four hours after I dropped the damn song, I received an email from the streaming company. Long, bullshit ass story short, Ronald intercepted the release of the song by using the fake contract he had. Basically, that meant that I couldn't keep the song on the streaming platform unless it was released under Ronald's weak ass company. I want to sit here and tell you that I was pissed off and was ready to get revenge in the worst way, but I can't. The truth is that my hands were tied and I was devastated. Ronald was playing a dirty game. He knew it and I knew it. He also knew that in order for me to play his dirty little game, I was going to have to lawyer up and I don't think he believed that I would. I'll keep it real, I didn't want to. I knew that lawyers were hella expensive and I knew that it would be a long process. I wanted a quick solution.

I started talking to people that I knew in the music industry, people that knew Ronald, and people that understood the business side of music better than I did. I would tell them everything that Ronald did and ask them for their advice on how to get my shit back or how to go about the situation in general without having to pay for a lawyer and everybody basically had the same bullshit answer: *it comes with the territory*. Literally not one person cared that a grown man had stolen my music from me and was refusing to let me see my streams or collect any of the money I had earned from them. In so many words, all of those muthafuckas told me that it would make for a good story one day. I didn't give a fuck about a good story. I had enough good stories to last a lifetime. I wanted ownership of my music. I wanted the money that was owed to me. I wanted at least one person to care that Ronald was violating me the way that he was. What I didn't want was to get a lawyer. But after weeks of telling my story to people who I thought would help me and not getting so much as a word of advice, I finally decided that it was time to lawyer up.

Shit, had Ronald not intercepted my single release for *'Obsessed'*, I may not have considered getting a lawyer because like I said, I was already willing to say fuck the whole *'Closure'* album and just start over – which is what I was literally trying to do. He left me no choice though. I decided that not only was I going to get the best lawyer I could find but I was also going to do everything I could to learn the ins and outs of the business side of the music industry. Music was my first love but if I'm honest, I never really took the time to learn the ins and outs of the business side of things because it wasn't something that ever crossed my mind. When you grow up on survival, you develop skills and learn about resources that contribute to your basic survival needs. You know most of the story of my upbringing so you know that my basic survival didn't require learning the business side of music. Lucky for me, one of the survival skills I learned was writing poetry which saved my life in more ways than one and ultimately led to me learning about the resources I needed in order to make music – like the studio, producers, engineers, the girl group etc. It wasn't until I was well out of survival mode and in a place of what some would call a life of luxury that I needed to learn the ins and outs of the business side of the music industry. It wasn't until my experiences with Ronald, that I realized I needed to learn everything I could.

As badly as I wanted to create and drop music, I couldn't. Not until I handled the Ronald situation. So, for the next couple of months, I researched everything that I thought mattered about music publishing, ownership, and distribution. I also researched entertainment lawyers until I came across one that I felt would be the best option for my situation. You have to remember that my situation had a lot of fucking layers to it; the initial contract that I signed when I was a kid, the super fraudulent contract Ronald sent to the streaming company, and most importantly, all of the money he was pocketing from MY music. I was able to find a lawyer that came highly recommended and seemed as though he truly understood my situation. As I expected, he was hella expensive but it was obviously the only way I was going to be able to end my contract with the devil so that I could be in control of my music career.

Financially, I was good but unexpected lawyer fees at more than ten thousand dollars was still wack. I really had to hustle my ass off so that I could get the money because I didn't want to have to tap into my savings to pay for it. I was increasing *Frost* inventory, hosting more, and doing paid brand partnerships to stack as much as I could, as quickly as I could. Every now and then, I would write a song, journal my feelings, or just write a poem, but I wasn't in the studio at the time. I wanted to be there, but I also knew that if I had music recorded, I would want to drop it, so to me, it just made the most sense not to record anything at all. Of course people would hit me asking when I was going to drop more music and it would always make me just a little sad, but I was in a legal battle that I couldn't even speak of and I was in it for the long haul.

AFTER ABOUT A YEAR – a very long year and about $45k I paid in lawyer fees – Ronald backed out of all of the lawsuits my lawyer filed against him on my behalf. It's funny because he probably made well over one hundred thousand dollars off my music but he couldn't afford to fight me in court. Those lawyer fees add up real quick and if you don't really got it like you say you got it, you can't keep up. I know his ass didn't think I would take him to court but he for damn sure didn't know that I could afford to do so. I'm not going to lie, the idea that Ron probably didn't think I could or would take him to court, actually makes the fact that I actually did it even better. Definitely could have used the money on something else, but I guess everybody was right– it made for a good story. In the end, I was able to get a few of my songs back but not all of them. However, I can finally release music again and I have complete ownership over every single song I drop. I could say that that's all thanks to Ronald, but fuck that nigga.

11

ON AGAIN OFF AGAIN

A FEW MONTHS went by and I finally decided to take a night off from working so that I could go to the club. Lindsay's new boo at the time got a table, so we were with him, his friends and a few of Lindsay's homegirls. I wasn't super lit because I didn't know any of the guys we were with. It was a cool vibe but it wasn't what I was used to. Anyway, I must have been there for all of an hour when out of nowhere, I got a text from Shawn asking me what I was doing.

Bitch, my stomach dropped into my ass because I honestly didn't think I'd ever hear from him again. At first, I considered not even responding because he fell back from us over nothing. Boy fuck you. You cut me off over some childish shit and now all of a sudden you want to know what I'm doing? Please. So anyway, I did what we all would have done, I replied immediately and told him I was out with my girls.

The last thing I was expecting was for him to tell me that he was in Atlanta, but that was exactly what he did. He was at another club and told me to pull up on him. I was trying to keep my cool because I didn't want Lindsay to see how excited I was to hear from Shawn. You know I always try to be strong on the outside. I also didn't want Shawn to know how excited I was to hear from him because I just didn't think it was necessary – always have to play the game, you know? After a few texts back and forth with Shawn about me meeting him at the club he was at, I took one last shot with Lindsay before I requested my *Uber*.

"Apparently Shawn is out here so I'm going to link with him right quick." I said to Lindsay after we took our shots.

"Oh. Cute. Ok. Bet. Be safe." Lindsay said without judging me.

Before heading outside to wait for my *Uber*, I went to the restroom to make sure I still looked like a bad bitch – and did.

I WAS SO nervous on the way over there because realistically, Shawn and I hadn't really known each other for that long. We had only actually spent like two and a half days with each other in person and then talked on and off after the whole incident. Mostly arguments and petty shit but for some reason we wouldn't leave each other alone. Like, what kind of love story is that? But none of that negates the fact that we had something real – even with all the bullshit. I wasn't really sure why Shawn suddenly had a change of heart, or what the plan was once I got to the club, but I was obviously willing to find out.

When I got there, I sent him a text message to let him know that I was out front and he sent his brother out to come get me. I had never met his brother before obviously, but apparently he knew who I was because once he came outside, he walked right up to me and quickly introduced himself.

"What's up? Travis." He said, extending his arm out so that I could shake his hand.

"Hey, I'm Winter." I said, shaking his hand.

There wasn't any other conversation after that, I just followed Travis into the club.

Once I got to Shawn's table, he was sitting on the back of the couch, so I stepped onto the couch so that I could be at his level. I was still super fucking nervous but I smiled at him as I took a few steps closer and then he stood up, grabbed my waist, wrapped his arms around me and gave me the biggest hug. I wrapped my right arm around his shoulders and held my dress in place with my left hand because he was holding me so tight that my dress felt like it was rising. He smelled so damn good and I missed his touch so much. It was like for a moment, nothing else in the world mattered. I was right where I was supposed to be.

Neither of us said a word while we hugged. I can only assume that he was taking everything in the same way that I was.

Shawn finally broke the silence when he said, "Let's take shots."

"Ok, let's." I said with a cheesy smile as I stopped hugging him.

Shawn poured shots for everyone at the table and then we all tapped our shot glasses together. The way he looked into my eyes made me want to jump on him right there in the middle of the club. I didn't, of course, but it was the moment I knew that he missed me just as much as I missed him.

We kept taking shots the entire night so we were super drunk but we were having so much fun. I was dancing on him all night, and he was hugging on me and just being super affectionate. Mind you, we were in the club, so it wasn't like we could really have a real conversation about anything. It was one of those times where 'what's understood doesn't need to be explained' made sense.

When we were getting ready to leave the club, I told Shawn that I was going to call my *Uber* so that we didn't have to wait too long.

He was like, "Nah, you're going with me."

Which is obviously what I wanted to do anyway, but we hadn't spoken for a while so I didn't know what type of time he was on. Anyway, me, him and his brother got into an *Uber* and the whole way to the hotel, Shawn was kissing all over me and rubbing my thighs and shit. We were obviously in love. No, I'm kidding. But we were definitely very happy to see each other, mixed with being stupid drunk.

When we got to the hotel room, Shawn realized that both he and his brother had left the room key inside of the room and we were so drunk that we couldn't stop laughing about it. You would have thought we were some little ass kids.

My feet started hurting, so I sat down in front of the room door and took my heels off. Shawn sat right next to me.

"Nigga, I will go to sleep right here." Shawn laughed.

I laughed too.

"Stay right there, bro. I'm going to get another key." Travis said.

"A true hero." I said sarcastically.

We were a mess. It was already a lot that I was barefoot but our drunk asses started laying down on the nasty ass hotel floor while we waited for his brother to bring the key up. Honestly, I don't even know how long it took for Travis to come back, but it felt like Shawn and I were laying there for hours while we laughed about absolutely nothing. It was a very pure moment of just being free and raggedy without any worries of the outside world.

When Travis finally came back with the key, Shawn got

up from the floor, grabbed my hand, walked inside the suite and led me right to his bedroom.

As soon as the door closed behind us, I dropped my shoes and Shawn grabbed my face and said, "I fucking missed you." Right before he kissed me.

We fucked all night and it was like we hadn't just gone so long without speaking to each other. Instead, it was like we picked up right where we left off and I loved every second of it. Sex is always better when you really care about the person you're fucking. So on top of us being super lit, the sex was fire. It was *always* fire and that's probably what drove your girl crazy.

The next morning, we woke up and were still laughing about the fact that we were locked out of the room and lying on the hotel floor. We just stayed in bed together for a while. He laid his head on my stomach and we just scrolled through our phones without saying a word. With anyone else I would have gotten up and left before they even woke up, but I wanted to soak in every moment with him. I studied his features from the shape of his nose down to the back of his ears. I felt at home and I knew I was in love with him.

Eventually, Shawn said, "Let's go to breakfast."

I wasn't prepared to sleep at his hotel, or even see him at all for that matter, so the only clothes I had were the dress and heels I wore to the club.

"You want me to go to breakfast in a dress and some heels?" I laughed.

Shawn laughed as he got out of bed and said, "Oh shit. You can just wear one of my t-shirts and heels. That way it's not super dressed up."

Even though I looked a true mess, that was cool with me so I took a quick shower, he let his brother know that we were all going to breakfast and then he took a shower and got dressed too. As we were getting ready to leave, he realized that he left one of his phones in the *Uber* the night before. Initially, he was just going to call the phone company and have them turn the phone off until he could go get another one but then I suggested that we at least try to track it first. Sure enough, it gave us a location and we took an *Uber* to the area where the GPS told us his phone was.

We were all cracking jokes about how we were on some mission trying to hunt down a damn phone but then when the driver dropped us off, we saw the car that we were in the night before. Me, him and his brother were laughing so hard that we had actually found the car but no one was in it, which made sense since it was still pretty early in the day. We turned on the phone's alarm from the *Find My iPhone* app and to all of our surprise it was in the car from the night before. There was only a few houses in the area, so we were like fuck it, let's knock on all the doors until we find the driver.

It didn't even take us long, either. The driver was super nice when we found him and apologized for not knowing that Shawn's phone was in his backseat. Not that it was his fault in the first place, but we did appreciate his willingness to allow us to grab it. I mean, it is hella weird that three random ass people are knocking on your door in the morning asking you to open your car door for them. Crazy. Anyway, we requested another *Uber* so that we could finally go to breakfast.

IT'S funny because I just assumed that Shawn would be less affectionate at breakfast than he was the night before since we were sober and out in public. I think that was a fair assumption given the fact that he acted like the world was ending when Lindsay thought he was my man but I was wrong. He was actually more affectionate at breakfast than he was in the club and I was eating that shit up–giving him that same energy. For me, it affirmed what I already knew: that I wasn't crazy to think that he fucked with me how I fucked with him when we first met. I was starting to think that maybe the reason he reacted the way he did about the photo and the convo with Lindsay was because he fucked with me more than he expected to. You know niggas will run from feelings if they can, so to me, it just seemed like that's what happened.

AFTER BREAKFAST, we went back to his hotel and slept. Shawn and I ended up spending the rest of the day together just laying around, watching movies, and ordering room service. It was a perfect and unexpected break from all that I had been dealing with as far as Ronald goes and how hard I had been working in general. But the truth was that it was so much more than that because I had missed him so much since all of our drama. His flight was later that night and I was not ready to go back to not seeing him or speaking to him again so I decided that I needed to tell him how I felt so that things didn't have to end when he left Atlanta.

We were still laid up – he was propped up by a couple of pillows and I was laying on his lap. I was going back and forth in my mind on whether or not I actually wanted to follow through with my decision to tell him my feelings and then I finally mustered up the courage.

"I think I'm falling in love with you. I know that sounds crazy 'cus we haven't spoken to each other or seen each other in so long but I just feel safe with you. It feels different with you." My heart was beating so hard and fast I felt like he could hear it.

Shawn looked down at me and said, "I don't believe you."

I'm sure you can imagine my confusion and my surprise, because what kind of shit was that? I should have taken that red flag and ran far away with it. But something about hearing it made me want to prove my love to be true. I had been through so much dark shit in my life that when "real love" came around I wasn't willing to lose it. I was willing to fight for it. I was willing to try to heal the seemingly broken man in front of me. Crazy enough, he didn't tell me that he loved me too or anything like that. We just had sex again and then before I knew it, it was time for him to go to the airport. So that was it. He was in Atlanta, I fell in love, and he went back to Michigan.

———

I WASN'T sure what to expect from Shawn once he was back in Michigan, but he called me as soon as he got home and for about a week, everything was going well. We'd talk on the phone every single day, he'd text me throughout the day and he was just being super cute and attentive. But, by week two, we were back to arguing. He would say little shit about how he could never trust anybody again and how since he lost the most important person to him he was never going to love anybody again either.

Obviously that shit got under my skin because there I was in love with him, thinking that he was basically feeling the same thing. Whenever he would say those things, I would try to reassure him that he could trust me and that one day he'd be able to love again. It was literally the same cycle over and over again until one day, he flat out told me that he would never be able to trust me after he heard that conversation Lindsay and I had. It was fucking annoying and strange that he couldn't let that conversation go because, again, it was really a stupid misunderstanding. I felt like I had proven that to him in every way I could but it seemed like he didn't want to see or accept the truth.

He would tell me things like *this is just all too good to be true between us. I know it will end bad*, or *I could count on one hand how many times we have had sex so it doesn't make sense.* He was actively trying to find an excuse as to why we couldn't be together and the excuses were breaking me.

Every other week we'd argue about the same shit. Him not being able to trust me and me not understanding why. My thing was like, ok, if you can't trust me then why do you keep coming back here? You know? It wasn't like I was begging that nigga to be with me. I was literally minding my business when he came back in the first place and would fall way back whenever he would tell me that he couldn't trust me. I really did love him but I wasn't about to beg a nigga to fuck with me when he was actively working to find a reason not to. So that became our cycle, good for a week, bad for a week. It was toxic but it was real so I just let it be what it was.

Now, I know you're probably wondering why I didn't just say fuck it to the whole situation but you have to understand that I really did see something different in him. Hell, I felt something different for him. I knew that he had been through a lot and because of that, I knew that it meant that he would display love differently. Not to say that it was an excuse for his childish behavior, but it definitely gave me insight. When things were good, they were really good. And when things were bad, they were bad but not the same type of bad that I had experienced in past relationships, so I was damn near willing to deal with the bad.

12

___

SPOOKY SEASON

BESIDES DEALING with my on again, off again relationship with Shawn, I was focused on my music, as per usual, but I was starting to want more from Atlanta. Everything was always work, work, work, and besides Lindsay and a few of her homegirls, I *still* didn't really have too many friends out there, so I couldn't really do much more than work. Even when I would host events, I was technically working. I wanted to do more things that made Atlanta feel more like home. I wanted to go to brunches and cute dinners. I wanted to go to the strip club with a homegirl just to have fun instead of with niggas to throw money. I just wanted to do regular shit sometimes. Don't get me wrong, I enjoyed Atlanta for what it was, but something was missing.

Since Halloween was coming up, I decided that I wanted to throw a party. I figured I'd rent out a venue and have one of the promoters I worked with promote it for me. When I came up with the idea, I texted Lindsay and said, *want to have a halloween party?* She sent me the heart eye emoji pretty much right away and said that she was down so we both started looking for different locations where we could have it. It was obviously going to be a Halloween theme but we wanted to throw the best party Atlanta had ever seen so we spent days looking at venues, decor, food vendors, all types of shit. I was really starting to look forward to it because I knew that it'd be a great way for me to meet more people but mainly turn the fuck up. The club shit is fun and it's even better that I get paid to do it but since I was itching for something different, and I was willing to come out of my own pocket to experience it, I wanted my party to be top tier.

During that time, Lindsay went out of town for two days for a photoshoot but she was still doing her part to get everything in order for our party. Being that it was my idea to have a party in the first place, I didn't expect her to come out of pocket for anything, I just wanted us to plan together. Plus, even though she always paid her portion of the bills on time, Lindsay was low key kind of cheap.

The night Lindsay left town for her shoot, me and Orien stayed home and watched movies while I made dinner. One thing I've always loved to do is cook, and I actually really appreciated being home that night for a home cooked meal. The only issue was that it left me too much time to sit with my thoughts and that never ended well for me. In order to silence my thoughts, I played some *Erykah Badu* and poured myself a glass of wine. Which of course, had me in my feelings about Shawn because you know that was something we bonded over when we first met.

Anyway, I was just vibing, cooking, and minding my business when I got a text from a number that I didn't recognize. The text simply said, *hey*. So I replied asking who it was. You wouldn't believe this but, it was Destinee. I hadn't talked to Destinee since she moved out. Like not a single peep from her, so I was surprised to see that it was her. I didn't really know what to say when she told me that it was her so I just said, *oh. Hey.*

The crazy thing is that seeing her name made me realize how much I had missed her. Me and Destinee had so much history and we went through so much together, so us ending our friendship and really not speaking again was actually pretty crazy. When she moved out, so many other things had happened and I was dealing with my own shit so I never really had time or made time to process the fact that she was gone. Truth be told, there wasn't even any bad blood, it was another thing that I just allowed to be whatever it was. After so many failed friendships and relationships, you sort of just become numb to that type of shit and that's exactly what happened with Destinee.

By the time I thought about how much I missed her, she sent me a whole essay telling me that she felt as though us not being friends was stupid because we had gone through too much to let something so small end our friendship. And she was right. We had plenty of arguments over the years but we would squash our beef in days, maybe a week or two, tops. But we had never gone months without speaking to each other.

After reading her text, I sent a reply that basically agreed with what she said and told her that we should just let the past go so that we could rebuild our friendship. I mean, I knew it wouldn't be hard for us to rebuild no matter how long we went without speaking, but I wanted to make sure Destinee knew that I agreed with her and was serious about letting the past be the past.

Now, my mama didn't raise no fool, so I wasn't trying to have Destinee move back in with me or anything. I just wanted us to get back to the solid ass friendship we had for so many years. The truth was that us falling off never really had to do with no damn Kevin Campos, it really had to do with how both of us reacted afterwards. When we had that big argument, I remember thinking about how crazy

Destinee had to have been for her to be saying the shit she was saying to me, but as I stood in the kitchen waiting for her to text me back that night, I realized that the things she was saying to me came from a place of her own emotions.

See, Destinee had her own bullshit to deal with. She's human just like you and me, with feelings and emotions and shit. When I really considered that, I realized that her empty threats to leave the apartment were rooted in fear of being kicked out. It was her way of protecting herself. My guess was that it was one of two things: if she left before I kicked her out, then she wouldn't have had to carry the embarrassment of getting kicked out. Or, the second option, she wanted me to fight for her to stay because it would somehow make her feel worthy. Both of those are just theories, but either way, I convinced myself that she was projecting her own insecurities onto me and that was yet another reason why we needed to squash the beef and continue on with our friendship.

Destinee needed my friendship as much as I needed hers. At some point in our lives, I had always told her everything. There was nothing about me or my adult life that Destinee didn't know and vice versa. We were genuinely best friends who always had each other's backs, who kept each other's secrets, and who shared each other's pain. Destinee was always there to listen to me cry about a nigga, and I was always there to hype her up so that she could build her self-esteem. There was no way we should have gone so many months without having that friendship in our lives. I say all that to say that I was really happy to hear from her and even more happy that we were able to put our differences aside so that we could get back to being best friends. Take it from me when I tell you that genuine friendships with girls are hard to come by. Sometimes you just have to be the bigger person and let the petty shit go in order to maintain that friendship.

Before I knew it, Destinee and I were on *FaceTime* all night long, updating each other on everything. She told me about a new business plan she was working on, I told her about Shawn, and even though she was living in Cali, I invited her to the halloween party. Remember, she had a few cousins in Atlanta and she would go visit them often so I knew that it was nothing for her to pull up to the party. Overall, it was cool being able to rekindle our friendship. It's crazy how sometimes you don't realize how much you miss somebody until they come back around. There was no need for apologies or anything like that because I think we had both come to the conclusion that our friendship was worth more than our problems. And that was enough for me.

The rest of the night was just about relaxation and reflection for me. If you haven't noticed, even though it seems like I avoid the things that bother me, I do reflect on life a lot. I reflect on my growth. I feel like it's important to reflect on how much you've grown because it helps you keep life in perspective. Sometimes we're hard on ourselves because we don't always see progress in the physical form. But the truth is that sometimes progress isn't visible. I think mental, emotional, and spiritual growth is more powerful than any physical or material growth. Think about a garden; the seed expands in the dark and then flourishes into something beautiful or fruitful. But, people only see beauty. They never see the roots that helped the garden grow. So, I reflect. I reflect to make sure that I can see the beauty of my roots. Reflection, next to heartbreak, is when I write some of the best shit I've ever written.

LINDSAY HAD FINALLY COME BACK HOME from her photoshoot and the first thing we did was go look at a few different venues to determine which one we liked best. After walking through three different locations, we ended up liking the first spot we saw the best and that's the one I booked. We were both excited because we just knew that it was the perfect spot. Afterwards, we went to lunch. Now, when I lived in LA and would go to lunch with my girls, we would always split the bill evenly. It never mattered who ate what or how many drinks any of us had, we just all paid an equal amount. I mean nine times out of ten, we all shared each others food and drank the same amount of alcohol anyway but even if we didn't who the fuck had time to do math over some fucking food and alcohol? With Lindsay, it was different. She always paid for her own shit, of course, but she would literally nickel and dime everything.

When I first met her, I didn't really think much of it because I just figured it was because we were new friends. But that shit never changed. For example, if we ordered a ten dollar wing appetizer to share, she would do some shit like eat one wing and say that she should only have to pay one dollar instead of five dollars since she didn't eat five wings. Like, bitch, we ordered it *together*, but ok! There was one time where we ordered a hookah and she felt like she didn't have to pay an equal amount because she didn't smoke as much as I did. It was very much broke bitch energy, but I knew she wasn't broke so I never understood it.

I say all that to say that when we went to lunch that day, we ordered a bottle of champagne in addition to our meals. Yes, I drank like two more glasses than she did, but we had agreed that we were ordering the bottle to share. Again, sharing means paying half and half, even if you don't actually consume half. So, when the check comes, I pull my card out and place it into the receipt book and instead of doing the same thing, Lindsay started calculating her food.

"We can just split it down the middle since we ordered

the champagne. The food probably comes out to be the same." I said, casually.

"Girl, you drank so much more champagne than me. I'm not going to pay half 'cus I didn't drink half." Lindsay laughed.

I couldn't believe it. I had never been bothered by her being cheap before and it wasn't like I couldn't pay for the bottle of champagne my damn self but that shit low key pissed me off.

"So then what was the point of suggesting that we share the bottle then? I could've just bought my own glasses. You always be trying to nickel and dime shit and that's weird. Like it's not even that serious." I said, trying to stay as calm as I could.

Lindsay just laughed and said, "Ok, girl. Relax."

There wasn't shit funny about being cheap and there wasn't shit funny about telling me to relax when I wasn't even turnt up. I should have knocked her fucking head off right then and there but I always try to give bitches the benefit of the doubt.

"No. Fuck a relax. You always do weird shit like this when it comes to paying for stuff. It's very weird. Next time we can do separate checks since you always want to play games." By that point, I was clearly very bothered from all the built up cheap shit she did.

Lindsay didn't say a word. She just kept laughing which really pissed me off but I didn't feel like dealing with drama because I was having a good day before she tried to play in my face. Plus, I knew that after our Halloween party she was going to be moving out, so I was just going to distance myself from her cheap ass as soon as she moved out.

FOR THE NEXT WEEK, I got over my irritation with Lindsay and we continued to get everything in order for our Halloween party because it was coming up fast. I had the promoters I knew posting about it for me, I had hella niggas posting about it and I had some strippers posting about it too because I hired them to dance at the party.

Everything came together perfectly. Destinee ended up flying in and pulling up with her cousins. My homegirl Brynn and a few of my other girls from LA came out, too. Everybody dressed up and had a good time. The strippers cashed the fuck out. The food was good. The bartenders and bottle girls I hired cashed out too. It was lit. It was worth every dime I spent and I was happy to have met so many people. I mean some of them were definitely weird and not people that I would ever spend time with but I felt like I had established some genuine connections overall and sort of made a name for myself in Atlanta because everybody had so much fun.

Brynn was the only one of my homegirls that ended up staying at my house with me. Destinee slept at her cousins house and everyone else had gotten rooms, or had niggas in Atlanta that they stayed with. We were all so drunk at the party that Brynn and I didn't wake up the next day until late afternoon. While she showered, I went into Lindsay's room to see how she was feeling. She drank so much at the party that I just knew she was going to be super hungover but when I walked into her room, she was actually packing everything up for her move. The blankets on her bed were all balled up, so I just sort of jumped in the pile as I said good morning to her and immediately realized that I had landed on something because I heard a very faint cracking noise. I assumed that I must have jumped on the remote or something because it wasn't very loud at all.

"Noooo!" Lindsay said as I plopped down on top of the pile of blankets.

"Oh, my bad. What was that? How do you feel?" I said, completely oblivious to what had actually happened.

"That was my TV! You for sure cracked it!" Lindsay whined.

"Aw shit!" I hopped off of her bed and ripped the blankets off fast as hell.

It was a very, very thin crack but I definitely cracked her TV screen. I mean it was obviously an accident because there was no way for me to know that the damn thing was underneath all of the blankets. And the reason I thought that I had landed on a remote or something small was because I had actually landed on the corner of the TV screen, cracking only a small section toward the edge.

"Damn. My bad. Don't trip. I'll buy you a new one." I promised.

To me, it wasn't that big of a deal since I was going to buy her another one. Like, yeah, it sucked to have your shit damaged but if you're getting a brand new one at no charge to you then fuck it. Realistically, it just meant that it was one less thing she was going to have to move from one apartment to another.

I guess Lindsay called herself being nice when she said, "I know you will, it's still annoying that you cracked it though. Like, moving is already so exhausting and this just adds one more thing to the list."

Little Miss Lindsay was working my last fucking nerve. Between being cheap and talking to me like she was fucking dumb, I was ready to slam her fucking head through the damn wall but instead, I kept it cute.

"Ok, Lindsay. Text me your new address so that I can go order you a TV right now and have it shipped to your new spot." I said with an attitude as I walked out of her room.

That was strike number two for Lindsay but I was still trying to be the bigger person. It wasn't like I shattered an urn with ashes in it or something; I cracked a cheap ass TV and said I'd replace it. In my mind I was like, get over it bitch, because I for damn sure wasn't about to go back and forth about it.

By the time I walked out of Lindsay's room and across the hall to mine, I was already over it. I laid across my bed and searched the internet for TV's so that I could be ready to hit purchase as soon as Lindsay sent me a shipping address. At that point, Brynn was done with her shower and had opened the bathroom door just enough for us to hear each other talking without having to yell. I continued to shop for TV's while Brynn talked about how lit the Halloween party was and how she was supposed to be going on a date with a guy that she had met there.

Brynn and I spent like five minutes recapping the night while she finished getting dressed and then she came and laid down next to me on my bed.

Out of nowhere, she said, "Winter, I feel so bad for putting Diamond on Xavier."

It took me a second to process what she said to me. One because it was random but two, because I wasn't sure I heard her correctly.

"Diamond on Xavier? Diamond like from the show, Diamond? On my Xavier? What do you mean?" I sat up.

Brynn sat up too. "Yeah. We were all at an event and I introduced them to each other but I thought Diamond knew that you had fucked with him for years, so I didn't think much of it."

Ok, so let me break this down for you real quick. Brynn and I had a bunch of mutual friends. I don't remember who initially introduced us, but we built our own relationship and had been friends for a couple years. She was also friends with Diamond, pretty much the only girl I was still cool with from the show. Diamond knew me well enough to know that Xavier was my man even when he wasn't my man. Hell, even a bitch that didn't really know me personally back then knew that Xavier was my nigga even if he wasn't.

What Brynn was telling me was brand new to me. I had never heard about Diamond and Xavier being a thing but I didn't want to make a big deal out of it because I didn't want Brynn going back to Diamond to tell her what she told me or anything like that. So once again, I just kept my fucking cool.

"Oh. It's whatever. Shit, this is the first I'm hearing of it, so it couldn't have been that much of a thing." I said nonchalantly.

The truth was that whether it was a big thing or a little thing, it shouldn't have been a thing at all seeing as though Diamond was supposed to be my friend. I can't tell you how many niggas I curved for the simple fact that I knew Diamond had fucked with them. As soon as a nigga slid in my DM's trying to shoot his shot, I would always let them know that I knew that they were Diamond's old nigga so we didn't have anything to discuss. That was on multiple occasions, not just once or twice. So even though I was acting nonchalant to Brynn, I was livid on the inside.

About twenty minutes after Brynn told me about putting Diamond on Xavier, she left my house to go on her date and I immediately started drinking. There's no hangover cure like drinking more and between Lindsay's broke bitch energy and Brynn telling me that my homegirl fucked my ex boyfriend, I was so irritated with how my day started. It only took me a good ten to fifteen minutes to get drunk again because realistically, I was probably still drunk from the night before.

The first thing my drunk ass did was call Diamond.

As soon as she answered the phone I said, "Hey, so did you fuck Xavier?"

She paused for a second and then said, "Who told you that?" As if she was skeptical.

That was the wrong fucking answer. "Ok, so you did. Bet. Bitch do you know how many times I've curved your niggas for you?!" There was no way I could hold back my anger with Diamond.

Diamond was still trying to act confused even though it was obvious that I knew it was true. "Who even told you that shit?"

"It don't even matter who told me. If that shit wasn't true you would have straight up said that. It's all good. You're dead to me." I said before I hung up the phone.

Alcohol and anger have never been a good mix for me and for some reason, I thought it would be a good idea to hop on the instigating ass internet to vent. At that point in my career and life, I knew better than to take any of my personal business to the internet but besides being drunk, I really just didn't give a fuck. So I made a couple of posts and hopped on Live and started talking about how bitches aren't loyal and how Xavier was dead to me too.

Diamond was really my friend and Xavier was literally the love of my life so underneath the alcohol and the anger, I was heartbroken. If nothing else, I was a loyal ass friend to Diamond and a loyal ass bitch to Xavier. Hell, I was even loyal to Xavier when we broke up. There were always lines I wouldn't cross, out of respect. Shit was about the principle. The way I was feeling that day though was that they could both go to hell.

I'm not going to lie, after I talked my shit on the internet, I cried. I turned my phone off for a few minutes, so that I didn't have to deal with the fucking blogs and I took a shower and cried some more. The same way I used to cry in the shower when I was a teenager. Yet another heartbreak. Yet another betrayal that came from somebody I loved wholeheartedly. I felt betrayed by Diamond because I genuinely had love for her, but Xavier knowingly fucking my friend after everything he and I had been through together was treacherous. Xavier really had no moral compass and I truly blame that on his rich kid syndrome.

Anyway, after crying in the shower and somewhat sobering up, I threw my hair in a bun, put on some sweats and decided to go for a drive. It didn't really matter where I ended up, I just needed to be away from everything and everyone for a second. Lindsay was in and out of the apartment moving all of her shit out and I didn't want to deal with that. Sitting in my room only forced me to think about how hurt I was. Unfortunately, I was about five minutes into my drive when I decided to turn my phone back on and started receiving all of the notifications from social media and text messages from my friends who were making sure I was good and trying to get the full story.

The one text I decided to read was a text from Lindsay because I knew that she wasn't about to be talking about the one topic I didn't want to talk about. To be honest, I can't remember exactly what the text said, but it said something about the broken TV. Whatever the fuck it said, she called me a bitch while she said it and that set me the fuck off. I literally pulled my car over to the side of the road because I was going to call her to find out where she was so that I could pull up and beat her ass. As I was getting ready to call her, I remembered that we were sharing our locations with each other.

See, I thought she would be smart enough to talk crazy to me when she was done moving her shit out but her location was actually pinging right at my apartment. Before I flipped a bitch to head back to my place, I called Brynn to see where she was.

"Hey. Where are you? I'm about to go beat this bitches ass, do you want to ride with me?" I said with almost no emotion.

Brynn was almost excited when she said, "Oh, bitch. Yes! I mean, I'm on a date right now but just come scoop me up and then I'll come back after. I'm right here at *Pappadeaux.*"

Pappadeaux was fairly close to my house so it was nothing for me to pick her up and then drop her back off to her date after I beat Lindsay's ass. All of my bitches are always down to slide when I need them to.

"Bet. I'll be there in like five minutes." I said through laughter because I couldn't believe Brynn was willing to leave her date at the restaurant so that she could watch me beat a bitch up.

She never even asked me who I was beating up or why; she was just down. When I pulled up to the restaurant, she was already standing in front. We both laughed hysterically as soon as she opened the passenger door.

"Bitch, are you serious?" I laughed. "What did you tell this man?"

Brynn was putting her seatbelt on. "Girl, I told him I'll be back in thirty minutes! So you have to do this shit quick. Come on!" She laughed.

It only took me about five minutes to get home but Brynn and I didn't say another word the whole way there.

"Here, hold this for me." I said as I unlocked my front door and handed Brynn my phone and keys.

When I opened the door, I expected to see Lindsay in the living room, but she wasn't there so I yelled, "Lindsay! I'm a bitch right?"

She didn't say anything, but I knew that she was in her bedroom so I walked through the living room, quickly opened her bedroom door and started socking her in the face as soon as I walked into her room. She was trying to fight back, but her shit wasn't landing and eventually, she gave up and kneeled down as she covered her head with her forearms.

"Now who's a bitch?" I yelled as I punched her in the head one last time.

She just stayed there, kneeled down on the floor looking sad.

"And you can buy your own fucking TV, bitch!" I said as I slammed her bedroom door on my way out.

Brynn was standing in the hallway with a front row seat of the ass whooping and just calmly handed me my phone and keys as we walked to the front door. When we got in the car to head back to *Pappadeaux*, both of us started laughing hysterically again. I don't think either of us were laughing at the fact that I beat Lindsay up, I think we were both laughing at the fact that Brynn left a date to watch me beat Lindsay up.

AS I PULLED up in front of the restaurant and Brynn took a quick look in the rear view mirror to make sure she still looked cute, she said, "Well, at least you got me back in less than thirty minutes! Bye, bitch! I'll call you later!"

And just like that, she was back inside of the restaurant.

Before I pulled out of the parking lot, I called Destinee so that I could tell her what had happened. Truth be told, I probably didn't have to beat that girl's ass like I did but she caught the right bitch at the wrong time. I let her shit slide way too many times and her calling me a bitch was the last fucking straw on top of the fact that I was pissed off about the whole Diamond and Xavier bullshit. So the only lesson I learned from that whole situation was that I needed to stop giving bitches passes.

13

SURVIVING R&B

BEATING LINDSAY UP was something I never saw coming. Like, usually you know that you're going to have to beat a bitch ass as soon as you meet her or get to know her a little, but I never saw that happening with Lindsay. I told you, besides randomly being cheap, me and her became really good friends and she was a good roommate too. But the truth is that I can't blame anybody but myself for that bullshit because I knew better than to get another roommate. I guess I should've listened to my intuition.

For the next few months, instead of getting a new roommate to replace Lindsay, I converted her room into part closet, part office. *Frost* was growing more and more and I was starting to have more ideas for its expansion, so having a home office allowed me to stay organized and efficient. It also helped me create some sort of separation in my mind between my music and my store. After another failed roommate situation, the only roommate I needed was Orien but I knew that if I didn't fill up Lindsay's room with something, I'd start to feel lonely. I didn't want to fill that void with another roommate.

When I had my Halloween party, I happened to meet a hairdresser named Tiffany who traveled between Atlanta and LA to do celebrity hair. She was super cool and mentioned that she had a photoshoot planned in LA that she wanted me to be a part of so we exchanged numbers. Usually when things like that happen, I take them with a grain of salt because most times people aren't prepared to execute their visions and are just saying shit just to sound or look like they have things going for themselves. Anyway, I say all that to say that when Tiffany reached out to me to request my rates for an out-of-town photoshoot, I was surprised. Not only was she prepared to pay my rate, her team was also prepared to book my flight and hotel as well. Her team was super organized and professional and I appreciated that because I love seeing other women be about their business and their bag. The shoot was going to be in LA on a Monday morning, but they were flying me out Friday night to make sure that we didn't encounter any types of delays with travel or anything like that, which was smart of them.

You know me, I'm about my business and my coin too, so I made sure to hit a few promoters I knew, to let them know I'd be in town and was available for hosting on Friday and Saturday nights. Obviously I was going to make the most out of being flown to LA. Since Tiffany and her team were on their shit, I wanted to make sure that I was just as much on mine, which was why I wasn't going to make myself available for any bookings on Sunday night. I didn't want to show up on Monday morning looking tired or feeling hungover.

———

MY FLIGHT LANDED in LA at about eight o'clock on Friday night and by that time, I had been booked to host a day party on Saturday, which was perfect. Even though I could have checked into my hotel right away, I went straight from the airport to Destinee's house. We didn't have any specific plans or anything, plus I don't know if I mentioned this but she lived with her dad at the time so we just planned to grab some food or something.

While we were hanging out, she kept trying to convince me to move back to LA. Her argument was that I made more money in LA than I did in Atlanta, there were more opportunities for me in LA than there was in Atlanta and that LA was where all my friends were. She wasn't wrong about any of the things she said, but she was also suggesting that we just get a place together and that's where she had kind of lost me. Yeah, our friendship had gone right back to normal, but I wasn't really sure that living with her again would be a smart move. It was definitely something to consider though, if for no other reason than the fact that LA really did have more opportunities for me than Atlanta did.

THE NEXT DAY my homegirl Janessa and a couple of her friends met me at my hotel so that we could all pre-game and pull up to the day party I was hosting. Janessa's homegirls were cute and they were fun to be around, so I was glad they came with us. We had the club turnt, as usual.

While we were partying, I got a text from Tony Tempo. Tony and I go way back. We met at a party one time and had just been friends for years after that. Whenever we were in the same city, we'd link but we never went out of our way to spend time with each other. When he hit me, he said that he saw I was in town and told me to pull up on him because he was having a little thing at his house. I told him that I'd pull up when I was done working. I was only with four other girls and they were all cute, so I didn't even bother asking Tony if it was cool for me to bring them with me because he had already told me he was having a get-together. Obviously if it was just going to be me and him, I would have gone to his house by myself.

My girls and I pulled up at Tony's about an hour after he and I spoke. His bodyguard, Beast, greeted us at the door and confiscated my friends' phones. See, Tony is a very popular musician, one of the best and most known in the world, so whenever he has parties at his house, everybody that comes, has to give their phones to security, unless you're close with Tony. It's how they make sure that what happens at the house never touches the internet — a very common precaution in LA. My friends weren't tripping though, especially because when we walked in, there weren't many girls there anyway so we knew we weren't going to stay long.

The first thing Janessa and her homegirls did was go to the bar while I looked around the house so that I could let Tony know that I was there. While I was looking for him, I ran into this white girl that looked so drugged out that I was surprised that Tony allowed her to be in his house. He was always pretty good about having bad bitches that could handle their liquor and knew when to leave their nose alone. This girl was super pale, her hair was greasy, she looked old enough to be somebody's auntie and she looked like a whole crackhead – nothing like me or any of my girls. It was hard for me not to stare at her but Janessa and her friends had made their way to the living room, where I was, and snapped me out of the trance the dirty looking white girl had me in.

At almost the same time that Janessa and her girls walked up to me, Tony came out into the living room.

"What's good, Winter?" He smiled as he hugged me.

"Hey, what's up?" I said, hugging him back.

When I stopped hugging him, I started to introduce my girls. "These are my girls…" I said before Tony cut me off.

"Where yo cup at?" He said, as he put his arm around me and led me toward the kitchen where the bar was.

"Stay here." I looked back at Janessa. "I'll be right back." I said.

"Man, I thought you were coming by yourself." Tony said. His tone was calm, but I could tell that he was genuinely bothered.

"Well, we were at a party. I figured you knew I was with bitches because you told me you were having a thing." I sort of laughed off the awkwardness.

"It's all good. They don't have their phones, right?" He asked as we reached the kitchen. He sounded paranoid and on edge.

"Nah. They gave their phones to Beast before we walked in." I was starting to get a little irritated.

The girls that were at his house weren't anywhere near as cute as the girls I brought with me so I didn't really understand what the issue was.

"It's cool. Just let me know next time." Tony said as he handed me a drink.

"Alright. My bad." I said as I took the drink and started walking toward the living room. "Ima make sure they're good. I'll be back." I said.

I was actually ready to get the fuck on so I was going to let the girls know that we were going to finish our drinks and then leave because I didn't like Tony's energy, there was a crackhead looking bitch walking around and overall, whatever he was supposed to be having wasn't lit at all.

It only took us about ten more minutes to finish our drinks before we started to walk toward the front door. I had no intention of letting Tony know that we were leaving because I didn't want him to try and convince me to stay. Unfortunately, as we were getting ready to walk out the front door, he saw us.

"Aye! Winter! Come here for a second. Come upstairs with me." Tony said as he motioned for me to follow him.

I took a deep breath and said, "Ok. But hurry I have to go, we have another stop to make."

I started to walk back inside the house and said to Janessa, "Give me five minutes, girl. I'll be right back."

And then I looked over at Beast and said, "Can you give them their phones? We're about to leave." As I pointed at Janessa.

Tony was already upstairs by the time all of that happened, so I quickly went up to his room where he was waiting. To be honest, I didn't really know why he wanted me to go upstairs with him because we had never messed around and there wasn't any type of top secret information we needed to discuss. I figured maybe he just wanted to say bye since we hadn't seen each other in so long.

When I walked into his room, he was standing near the doorway so he closed the door behind me and smiled. "How you been, man? It feels like I ain't seen you in forever."

"I'm good. You know I moved to Atlanta, so I'm just out there recording music and stacking my money." I said as I sat on the edge of his bed.

He sat in a chair that was placed diagonally across from his bed.

"That's good. Yeah, when I saw you were in LA, I was like damn, we have to link." Tony said.

The conversation was super casual and pointless but I just figured he wanted to catch up because we really hadn't seen each other in a while.

"Yeah, for sure. Ay! Who's that white girl down there? Is she ok? Sis did not look good at all." I said. Part of me was concerned and the other part of me was actually confused.

Tony's energy completely changed. "What the fuck? That's been my friend a long time! I was there when her dad died and all kinds of shit. Don't ask me about no bitch!" He went from calm to furious in half a second. It was the strangest thing I'd ever seen.

I had never seen that side of Tony before. Of course I had heard a few things from the blogs about him being a monster but until that moment, I had never seen any of those characteristics. He didn't necessarily scream, but the way his jaw clenched, he could've shattered his teeth. His eyes became glossy and it was like he wasn't even looking at me anymore, he was looking through me. I was scared. Like, real life scared. It took me back to the day that Cinco had beat my ass so in that moment, I stood up.

"I was just asking. Chill the fuck out." I said super calmly as I took a step toward his bedroom door.

I wish I wouldn't have said those words. As soon as I took that step and said those words, Tony grabbed me by my neck with one hand and applied so much pressure that I couldn't breathe. I tried my best to remove his fingers from around my neck but his grip was so tight that I wasn't even able to create any type of space between his fingers and my skin. My heart was racing and my eyes were starting to tear up because no matter how many times I smacked his wrist, Tony wasn't letting up. It wasn't until I scratched his face that he released his tight grip from around my neck and when he did, I thought that I was going to be able to leave. But I was wrong. Instead, Tony wrapped my hair around his hand, body slammed me into the floor like I was a fucking rag doll and started hitting me in my face while he dragged me to his bedroom door. Naturally, I was trying my best to fight back but I didn't really stand much of a chance. I was screaming for him to get the fuck off me but it seemed like no one could hear me. I literally thought that I was going to die.

Me trying to fight back only pissed him off more. It was like every time I hit him, he would hit me harder until finally he dragged me into the hallway. He hit me in the face once more while my hair was still wrapped around his hand. When he managed to drag me to the top of the stairs, is when I started screaming even louder.

"Beast!" Tony yelled. "Yo! Beast!"

"Let me go, you bitch ass nigga! Let me the fuck go!" I screamed.

Beast had finally made it up the stairs to where Tony was beating my ass and he gave me a bear hug as if he was trying to calm me down before he carried me down the stairs. I was still kicking and screaming as Beast carried me. In some part because I was angry but in some part because I was scared. When we got to the bottom of the stairs, Beast placed me onto my feet but had a firm group on each of my shoulders.

"I'm sorry. I'm so sorry. You're ok, alright? You're ok." Beast tried to calm me down.

I didn't have words besides, "Let me go! Let me go!"

"Ok. I'm sorry. I'm so sorry." Beast said as he guided me toward the front door.

Beast was apologizing to me as if he knew that to be Tony's behavior. He didn't seem shocked or confused, it was like he knew what happened because it had happened before.

Beast didn't push me out of the front door, but he definitely made sure that I was all the way out of the house before he closed the door behind me and locked it. Janessa and her homegirls were scared and upset.

"What the fuck just happened?!" Janessa said.

"I'm calling the fucking police right now!" Her homegirl said with a shaky voice.

"No! No-no-no!" I yelled as I placed my hand over her phone screen. "Come on, y'all. Let's just go!" I said.

The five of us rushed over to Janessa's truck and left Tony's house as soon as we all hopped in. I told the girls what happened on our way to my hotel and begged them not to tell anyone.

When we made it to my hotel Janessa and the girls wanted to come up with me, but I told them I would be fine and that I just needed to sleep it off. I mean realistically, there wasn't really much they could do for me anyway. I think some part of me was embarrassed for myself. I was angry that another man had put his hands on me. I was angry that another man had violated me in a way that made me fear for my life and question whether or not men are really capable of protecting women. I was angry and embarrassed that once again, I was a victim. So instead of allowing the girls to comfort me, I pretended I was okay. I made them believe that it wasn't really that big of a deal even though it was.

As I stood in the hotel elevator to go up to my room, a lump formed in the back of my throat as I held back tears. Naturally my mind started to travel back. Back to the days when Cinco would beat on me. When I spoke about that, no one believed me. All of his friends said that I was a liar looking for attention. When he died, they shunned me for posting my condolences because they felt as though I lied on him. Not once did anyone ever have a real conversation with me about what happened. Not once did anybody ask me any questions that allowed me to vindicate my truth. Instead, they outcasted me and called me a liar because, let them tell it, there was no way in hell their beloved Cinco could have ever done something like that to me. Shit, not even his punk ass baby mama, who I protected, spoke up for me. None of that mattered at the time because I knew that I was telling the truth, but it didn't change the fact that not being heard or believed, added turmoil to the trauma. So with that, I knew that telling anyone about Tony would have been pointless. Cinco didn't even have any fame and no real fortune and nobody believed me. So, why the fuck would anybody believe me if I told them Tony was a drugged up, violent monster?!

Once I finally made it to my hotel room, I lost my shit. As soon as the door closed behind me, I fell to my knees and started to cry. Hard. The fear or adrenaline had started to wear off and my head started to throb. When I was able to find the strength to stand up again, I walked to the bathroom so that I could look at myself in the mirror. My hair was disheveled and my face was turning red. I knew that it meant I would start bruising by the time I woke up which was no good for the whole ass photoshoot I was in town for in the first place. Not to mention my nails were all broken and bloody from trying to fight back and there was a huge red mark on my neck from where Tony choked me. My knees were scratched, and bruised from being dragged as well.

While I was standing in the bathroom looking at myself in the mirror, I got a text message. My heart sank because it was from Tony. I took a deep breath before opening the message.

The text was straight to the point. *Hey, did you make it home?*

That shit blew my fucking mind. I couldn't believe he would even fix his bitch ass fingers to text that to me.

Are you out of your fucking mind you bitch ass nigga?! You just beat the dog shit out of me and you want to know if I made it home?! I texted back.

Tony was more of a monster than I knew.

Listen, I don't know what you think happened but you had a lot to drink so you may be a little confused. Get some rest and let's talk tomorrow. His text said.

I slammed my hands onto the bathroom counter out of anger. If niggas don't have shit else, they always have the fucking audacity. Tony and I had known each other for so many years and during that time, there were a number of situations in the blogs that eluded or directly stated that he was an abuser. The thing was that I never experienced that version of him. Up until that day, he was always super chill and fun to be around. Reality started to set in that Tony Tempo, the musician that every bitch in America knows and loves, the man that will sing a bitch right out of her panties was in fact the abuser that the blogs said he was.

The adrenaline had finally worn off completely and my face started throbbing with pain while I stood at the bathroom sink. I stood in the mirror reflecting on my poor judgment of character, wishing that I didn't always try to see the good in people because it always costed me. Tony was yet another nigga to add to the list of disappointments at my expense but I couldn't allow that to cost me a photoshoot too.

After about five minutes of reflecting on Tony's actions and reminiscing on the very similar circumstances I had with Cinco, I decided to block Tony and turn my phone off. I know, I let him off easy, but at the time, I wasn't concerned about punishing him, I was only concerned about moving forward. I didn't have time to be a victim.

After I turned my phone off, I turned the shower on and slowly took my clothes off. My body ached from being thrown around, so, slow was the only way I could do anything at that point. The water wasn't even hot yet, but I stood underneath the cold stream of water because I wanted to cleanse myself of anything that had to do with that day. Instead of waiting for the water to heat up on its own, I turned the faucet to the hottest it could go and tears started to rush down my cheeks. I knew that once again I would never get justice for what had happened to me. I knew that if I told the public about what that man did it would be flipped into me being a "liar" or "trying to bring a successful man down." I was helpless and angry so I washed my hair, cleaned my body and allowed my tears to intertwine with the stream of shower water and then I just stood there; numb.

I know that you're used to me acting like shit doesn't phase me, but it does. It always has. I mean, the real shit. Not hating ass bitches or anything like that. I'm talking about the people and things that I put my heart, trust and loyalty into. Those are the things that have an impact on my mental and emotional well being. I think that sometimes people forget that even though I come off as strong, the other side of me is sensitive and too forgiving. Deeper than that, another part of me is a wounded child hoping that just once in this lifetime I can feel a love that is pure and reciprocated, you know? I just want to experience a friendship, a relationship, a partnership, anything that won't betray me. But so far, I've never felt that so it's fuck these niggas and fuck these bitches too.

I ALLOWED myself another ten minutes under the water and then I got out. I wrapped my hair in one towel and my body in another before I turned my phone back on. As much as I wanted to stay disconnected for the rest of the night, I couldn't. For one, I needed to make sure that I was available in case anybody from the shoot needed to contact me, but two, I had contractual obligations to post on social media.

While the phone was loading, I was praying that I wasn't about to receive hella notifications about what Tony had done to me. I knew that Janessa wouldn't tell anyone, but I didn't know her friends well enough to know whether or not they would keep their mouths shut like I asked them to. It felt like I waited hours for that damn phone to load. That's how nervous I was. But luckily, there were no notifications besides a text from Destinee asking me if I wanted to go out with her. Of course I told her I couldn't, but I blamed it on an early call time for the hair shoot. That was only partially the truth though because it was Saturday and my shoot wasn't until Monday. The other part of that was because my face was already starting to bruise and I didn't want to tell her what happened. All I wanted to do was handle my business, get my money and then take my ass back to Atlanta.

WAKING up the next morning was hard. My body was hurting like I had been hit by a bus and my head was pounding like I was hungover. The first thing I did was open the front facing camera on my phone so that I could see the damage Tony had done. My eyes started to water up when I saw how many different areas on my face were bruised up. I guess the good news was that it didn't feel as bad as it looked but either way, I knew that the make-up artists were going to have to spend extra time covering up all the scratches and bruises before the shoot which was both annoying and embarrassing. I was hoping that by the end of the day, some of the bruising would go away. My bottom lip was a little swollen too but luckily, it was the entire bottom lip, not just one side of it so it was giving lip injection as opposed to assault and battery. I literally just stayed in bed that entire day. I ordered room service, watched movies, and iced my face hoping that it would help.

Unfortunately, the next morning I still woke up with hella bruises. I didn't have time to sulk in my sorrows, which was probably for the best. Plus, you know that I don't let shit stop me from getting to the money and I for damn sure wasn't going to let bitch ass Tony be the exception. Now, putting the bullshit behind me, getting out of bed and showing up to my shoot in good spirits with positive energy wasn't easy, but I got it done. Just like I expected, the make-up artists had to spend a little extra time making sure that my bruises were covered which means that I had way more make-up caked on my face than I normally would have. However, the focus of the shoot was hair, so even though my make-up was important, my hair was the main character.

Come to think of it, not one single person on that set asked me what happened to my face that day. They all just did their job, took extra care to be gentle when they worked on or around the bruised areas and made sure that I was comfortable. I can only assume that the reasoning was because they were used to shit like that, which is actually disgusting, but not surprising. Anyway, I killed the shoot, of course, which lifted my spirits but I was really happy to be done so that I could get back to Atlanta.

WHEN I MADE it back to Atlanta, I went straight home from the airport. For two whole days, I didn't talk to anyone or leave my house for any reason. Ya girl just needed to reset. When I finally decided to come out of my dark hole, I called Destinee. At first, I just wanted to talk about regular shit. Like, I just wanted to take my mind off of anything that had depression energy so before I even dialed her number, I had no intention of telling her what Tony had done to me.

That changed real fast when I heard her voice.

"Hey, boo." Destinee answered.

"Hey…" I said.

My voice cracked a little and even though I only said one word, the way that I said it was heavy. Anyone who heard me would have known that I wanted to say more than just *hey*.

Destinee knew. "Aw shit. What happened?" She asked.

I paused for a moment so that I could pull myself

together and tell Destinee that everything was fine. Instead, "I saw Tony Tempo when I was out there." I said.

"Oh. Ok. How was that?" Destinee was clearly confused.

"He beat my ass so bad that I could barely get out of bed to go to my photoshoot. But don't worry, he was polite enough to ask me if I made it home safely like two hours later." I tried to laugh it off but I started to cry instead.

Destinee was shocked. "Winter. What the fuck?"

Neither of us said a word while I cried over the phone.

"Did you tell the police? What happened? Where were you guys?" She broke the silence.

"No. What's the point? We were at his house. I don't even know what the fuck happened. We were in his room talking before I left and then he got mad that I asked him about some crackhead looking bitch that was downstairs. Des, I literally just asked if she was good. That's it. And then he lost his fucking mind he had to be high on something." I said through tears.

"Fuck." She said.

We were silent again.

"What if you move back to LA? So that you're not alone. I mean, I just think that you need to be closer to us – all your friends. We can get a spot together. I just ... I don't know Winter, I feel like you shouldn't be alone." Destinee was concerned.

I took a deep breath. "I'm fine Des. Don't tell anybody I told you that, ok? That stays between us. I wasn't going to tell anyone. I don't even know why I told you, but I'm fine. Everything is fine. I guess I just needed to get that out. I'm already over it."

"Ok. Well, if you change your mind, you know I got you." Destinee reassured me.

Having Destinee back in my life felt like perfect timing. Somehow, telling someone that wasn't there the night Tony put his hands on me was sort of a relief. Janessa was a good friend and I could have very easily spoken to her about it all since she was there but I didn't want to. Shit, telling Destinee was damn near an accident but it was one that happened to work out well because I didn't know that I needed it so badly. I'm not sure why, but telling her helped me feel better. And, I can't lie, for a second, I did consider getting a place with her because she was right, I shouldn't have and didn't want to be alone. But, at the same time, I needed to be alone so that I could do some soul searching.

14

REVOLVING DOOR

WHILE I SPENT the next couple of months trying to heal, soul search, get money and make music, Shawn and I were still doing the whole on-again-off-again thing. We were off during my Surviving R&B era and I didn't ever tell him that it happened because we had our own bullshit to deal with. And let me tell you, going back and forth with Shawn was annoying as fuck but there was no one to blame but myself because I was a willing participant in the fuckery. Of course I had other niggas here and there, but I didn't feel the same type of spark with any of them the way I did with Shawn. Besides that, none of them had dick as good as he did either. To be honest, I had so much going on at the time that pulling the revolving door of toxic love off the hinges wasn't really on the top of my list of things to do.

The thing with Shawn and I was that I loved him and I know he loved me but we were both toxic. Our connection was undeniable though. The love I felt for him was similar to the love I felt for Xavier when he and I were together and that was always how I knew that Shawn and I were special. As far as I was concerned, he could have been my soulmate and I wanted nothing more than for us to get our shit together so that we could just be all happy and in love and shit. The fact that he was in Detroit and I was in Atlanta didn't really help our situation much because he was busy with meetings, interviews, practice and games and I was busy traveling back and forth from Atlanta to LA for work. On top of traveling back and forth for work, there was just too much going on for both me and Shawn for us to spend any real time with one another. I mean, we spent a lot of time on *FaceTime* every day to make up for it but the cycle was the same, good for one week then beefing the next.

At some point, Shawn and I decided that we needed to make a real effort to spend time together and we were planning for him to fly me out to Detroit. It was perfect timing because I had also decided that I wanted to take Destinee up on her offer. I was in LA more than I was in Atlanta and I still didn't have many friends, or know too many girls that I vibed with in Atlanta so it just made more sense. Getting a place with Destinee didn't seem like an awful idea because I knew that if I needed to break the lease and get my own place, I could do that without a problem. But we had both grown so much individually and as friends that I was confident it'd work out. Moving back to LA also meant that I was going to be further away from Shawn than I already was and I felt like that was something I needed to tell him in person.

Planning on going to Detroit to see Shawn and waiting to tell him that I was moving back to LA somehow made it so that I was more ready than ever before, for us to be an actual couple. I wasn't trying to hold off on having that conversation with him in person though so one morning when I woke up, I called him and got right to it.

"Babe, are we going to do this forever, or are we actually going to grow up and be in a real relationship? Cus I'm not a play house ass bitch, so let's figure this shit out." I said as soon as he answered the phone.

Shawn was obviously irritated. "Why can't you just be happy, bro. We're doing good right now. Shit is fine. You're about to come out here soon, so just chill out, man. Let's just enjoy the fact that we aren't fighting right now." He said.

I mean, overall he was right because we had been in a good space for about three weeks, but also, fuck him. Men always try to tell women that they're doing too much when a woman asks for something he can't or won't provide. I wasn't asking him for a car, a house, a baby, shit, I wasn't even asking for a purse. All I wanted was the certainty that he was for me the same way that I was for him so that we could just be together. I wasn't doing too much. I wasn't asking for too much. Plain and simple, I was just asking the wrong nigga.

Anyway, the rest of our conversation was pretty pointless that day but I did my best not to rain on our little three week parade because I was still looking forward to flying out to see him. Over the next week or so, I started to pack up my apartment and ship small items to Destinee's house here and there so that my move wouldn't be such a struggle. And then I ended up having to fly to LA so that I could sign the lease for our new place. Of course, the apartment was going in my name because my credit was best, so that postponed my trip to Detroit a little. I had to tell Shawn that I was going there for work because I still hadn't told him that I was moving to LA. Truly a mess.

At first, I was devastated that I was about to go yet another week without seeing Shawn and then he suggested that since he was going to be in DC for a few weeks, he could just book me a flight to meet him there instead of going back to Atlanta after I handled my business. Obviously I was down because I missed him. Then I realized that another week of not seeing him gave me time to figure out what gift I was going to get him. I wasn't able to see Shawn for his birthday so I wanted to surprise him with something thoughtful to make up for it. That's the thing about dating rich men, you can't really buy them shit because they can buy everything for themselves. I knew I had to get creative to impress him which really wasn't an issue cause you know your girl is artistic and shit.

After some thought I came up with the idea to make Shawn a character of his own comic book and blow it up into a frame. I hit up a super dope artist in LA and asked him to make my vision come to life. I was excited because I knew that Shawn was going to love it and I genuinely enjoyed seeing him happy.

Sure enough, three days after I ordered the painting, Shawn told me that his plans changed and we would have to postpone our visit once again. I damn near wanted to cry when he told me because I missed him so much, I wanted to see him so bad and I needed to tell him that I was moving back to LA.

"Babe, I'm sorry. I gotta handle some shit but I'll make it up to you." He told me.

"It's cool. I just miss you but it's all good." I was trying my best to hide my disappointment.

"I know. I got you a gift. You gone love it. Seriously it'll make up for all this bullshit, I promise." Shawn sounded sincere.

There wasn't much I could do about the fact that we were about to go even longer without seeing each other. My feelings were hurt and I had an attitude, but we were still on a record streak of no arguing and I didn't want to be the one to ruin that. Plus, I was invited to a party that was happening that same night so I knew that I would be able to distract myself. Shawn and I weren't in an exclusive relationship because that's not what he wanted. Therefore, my options were still open and I wasn't obligated to tell him anything about being invited to an NFL players party. His bad. These niggas get a bad bitch and act like they forgot that everybody wants a bad bitch.

AFTER I GOT over the fact that I wasn't going to see Shawn for who knew how much longer, Destinee and I spent part of the day looking at furniture online. Surprisingly, I was excited to move back to LA and even more excited to be moving in with my best friend again. It was sort of like another fresh start even though I had already had hella fresh starts in LA in the past. Atlanta was good to me. I loved the city and I think that moving there to heal was definitely good for me but it was just time for another change.

I never would have guessed that I'd be moving into an apartment with Destinee again, but that was a huge part of the change. You know I can be cautious when trusting, so choosing to put another place in my name after what happened the last time was a different level of growth for me. Not that she could have put the apartment in her name if she wanted to, but putting it in my name gave me a sense of security in my decision. After so many years of crashing on different couches as a teenager, I had always been the one whose name was on a lease and whose apartment somebody would move into. I never wanted to feel like I was over-staying my welcome anywhere the way that I did when I was couch surfing so I have always made sure that any place I laid my head was a place that was fully mine. I wasn't having any second thoughts about moving back to LA, but signing that lease was sort of my way of making sure that I didn't change my mind about it.

I WAS low key excited about the party that night because I needed to take my mind off missing Shawn. Whenever I say I want to take my mind off a man, it doesn't mean that I'm going outside to find a new nigga. It just means that I am ready to turn up and intentionally not think about whatever man has me fucked up at the time. With that being said, I made sure that my makeup was on point, my hair was flawless, I smelled rich and luxurious and my dress was damn near painted onto my body before Destinee and I left her house to go to the party.

We were a little late getting there, but that was on purpose because we didn't want to have unnecessary conversations with people while we waited around for more people to show up. One thing about LA is that a majority of the time, you're going to see all the same niggas and all the same bitches at pretty much every party you go to. There's nothing wrong with that, but it can get repetitive. As soon as we walked in, we ran into a few bitches that I used to party with when I moved to LA the first time and they poured shots for us off the rip. Destinee and I had to play catch up so that we could be as turnt as all of the other girls but we didn't mind at all.

About an hour into the party and who knows how many shots later, the section we were in had all of the fine bitches in it. Surprisingly, I didn't know most of them but they were all super friendly. There was one girl in particular named Mercedes that kept talking to me the whole time but it was cool because we were all just having fun.

"Oh my gosh! Take a shot with me! Shawn Davis is over there and I just got so nervous!" Mercedes slurred her words.

My first thought was that there was no way in hell she

meant *my* Shawn Davis but I didn't want to jump to conclusions or prevent her from spilling any tea.

"Pour up, bitch! Why are you nervous?! Don't let these niggas make you nervous, sis!" I said as I held my glass out toward her.

"Ahh! I know! We've been dating for like a month now and he did not fucking tell me he was going to be here tonight when I told him I was coming here." Mercedes whined.

Confused, I said, "Shawn Davis? Oh! You must mean his brother, Travis Davis."

There was no way in hell.

"No, girl. Look." She turned my body around and then pointed towards Shawn. "Shawn Davis, he plays in Detroit."

My heart sank into the pit of my stomach. She was definitely talking about *my* Shawn. Men are so fucking embarrassing it's unbelievable. Granted, I didn't tell him that I was going to that party the same way he didn't tell me but the fact that a bitch was talking about dating him for a month was crazy. And the fact that he was in LA at the same time as me and didn't tell me was even crazier.

"Oh. Yeah. That is Shawn. You're fucking with him?" I asked calmly.

"Yeah. He saw me, too. His ass is acting like he didn't though." She said as she took her shot.

I laughed a little. "That's 'cus he ain't shit."

Immediately after that, I stormed over to Shawn. He saw me walking over to him but he didn't move a muscle because he knew what type of time I was about to be on.

"What the fuck nigga? You canceled my fucking trip just to end up in the same city as me and not say shit?" I yelled over the music.

Shawn shook his head in disappointment. I don't know why the fuck he was disappointed but he stood up and placed his hand on my back so that he could push me to an area where we wouldn't be seen. As soon as we were out of the way, I pushed his hand off of me.

"So you been fucking that bitch I was talking to for the last *month*?!" I yelled again.

I didn't even give him the opportunity to answer my question. "So that's why you been too busy to see me, huh? That's why we can't do this shit for real, huh? Cus you're a bitch ass nigga that can't keep it real and can't stop fucking with these thirsty ass bitches!" I was pointing my finger in his face while I yelled at him.

Shawn wasn't saying anything that meant anything to me at the time but he knew he fucked up.

Eventually, I stormed off and saw him go back inside. Destinee came rushing outside.

"Bitch, what happened?" She said as she walked toward me.

"Shawn is a bitch. Don't ever let me speak to him again. He got me fucked up. That's what happened." I said.

Destinee didn't know what to say, so she didn't say anything at all.

"Come on. Let's go. I don't have time for this shit." I grabbed Destinee's arm and pulled her toward her car.

I sat in silence the entire car ride back to Destinee's house. My heart was broken. I was more hurt that night than I had ever been hurt by Xavier. I couldn't believe that after all the time I spent trying to prove my loyalty and display my love for Shawn, it was all in vain. I made sure that Destinee couldn't tell that I was as heartbroken as I was, but I was dying on the inside. The way I was feeling had me wishing I didn't sign that lease because I felt like I didn't want to be around so many people that I knew all the time. I just wanted to crawl into a hole and die. I was so embarrassed and hurt.

When Destinee and I made it back to her house, I told her that I was annoyed with Shawn so I just wanted to shower and go to bed. She didn't ask any questions or anything, she just gave me a towel and a washcloth and told me that there was tequila in the kitchen if I wanted to drink a little more. I declined the tequila. Instead, I played some *Erykah Badu*, got in the shower and cried like I always did when I was heartbroken and pissed off. In my mind, it was the end of Shawn and I. There was no coming back from the way that I responded to his disrespect and there was no coming back from the fact that he disrespected me. All that was left was unanswered questions, feelings of betrayal and a broken heart full of love that had nowhere to go. Normally when I get my heartbroken, I leave all my tears in the shower but I was so hurt that I even quietly cried myself to sleep, hoping Des didn't hear me.

The next morning, against my better judgment, the first thing I did was hop on *Live*. Thinking back on it, it's actually funny because I've never been a 'if you know better, you do better' type of bitch. It's always been 'I'm going to do whatever the fuck I want, when I want', because I'm a hardheaded ass bitch. Anyways, I hopped on *Live* to give the girls a story time. My life is and has always been a movie and sometimes I just want to share that with people because I really couldn't make this shit up if I wanted to.

Instead of using real names, I gave Shawn and Mercedes fake names. Shawn and I weren't public with our situation and besides that little blog shit that happened when we first started hanging out, no one really knew that we were even dealing with each other. Therefore, I was confident that no one would know who I was talking about. I had to give a quick synopsis on mine and Shawn's relationship before I got to the part about him being at the same party as me but that probably made the story even better because from what

I could always tell, my followers have always loved my story times.

So anyway, maybe five minutes into the story time, everybody started dropping comments in the chat with the names of niggas they thought I was talking about. At first, they were loud and wrong and then somehow, they started to guess correctly. I tried my best not to change my demeanor so that they wouldn't know that they had guessed the right person, but there was so many comments that said Shawn that I had to wrap that shit up and log the fuck out.

Of course I didn't care that so many people had guessed correctly but it definitely wasn't my intention for that to happen. If Shawn didn't want his name attached to fuck boy shit, then he shouldn't have been doing fuck boy shit in the first place. The math is very fucking simple. I know his notifications were probably going crazy too because mine were. I was getting hella text messages, comments and DM's from people. One DM came from Marissa Jackson, a girl that had done the same show I did a few seasons before me. She was asking me if I was ok and said that she had seen me arguing with Shawn the night before.

When stupid shit goes even a little viral on the internet, you sometimes feel like you're alone. It's not like you're scared or incapable of standing up for yourself, you just feel like you're at the mercy of tens of thousands of people who have no life, no money and nothing but time to create bullshit narratives around something so simple. I say that to say that when I saw Marissa's DM, I felt a sense of relief because I knew that she knew what it was like to be attached to bullshit. As soon as I read her DM, I sent her my number and told her to call me as soon as she could.

"Hey, girl. It's Marissa." She said when I answered the phone.

"Hey. How are you?" I replied.

"I'm good. I just hit you because I saw you arguing with Shawn Davis last night at the party and then I saw you go live today kinda talking about it, so I just wanted to make sure you were good. I know this internet shit can be too much sometimes." She sounded sincere.

"I'm not worried about no broke internet bitches. Thank you for hitting me though. I appreciate that." I said.

Marissa and I didn't know each other but like I said, because we both did the show, we automatically had some sort of camaraderie. However, I had no intentions of confiding in a stranger about my business, I really just wanted to know what she had seen at the party and gauge what her take on it was.

Marissa gave me some unwarranted advice. "Well, listen. Shawn is a good look. Being attached to a Davis brother will raise your fucking stock. I don't know what beef you have with him, but it was very obvious that y'all have been rocking for a while. You hit a lick with that one, so use this internet attention and the shit y'all have going on to your advantage. Shit, this is your meal ticket, so eat, sis."

Marissa's advice was giving broke bitch energy and I hated that for her but it made complete sense as to why she felt the need to reach out to me in the first place. She wasn't trying to support me or make sure I was ok, she was just being a nosey bitch.

"Oh, girl, I get money. I don't need to come up off a nigga for that. Shawn just tried to play in my face yesterday and I had to let him know that I'm not the one. That's all. It was really simple." I said very nonchalantly.

"Ok, girl. That's cool. I just wanted to make sure you knew what type of bag you had." She replied.

"Oh yeah, no. The bag is with me. Fuck them niggas." I said with a fake laugh.

After that, Marissa and I got off the phone. I was more

irritated after speaking with her than I was from reading the hate messages I was getting. But I didn't have much time to be bothered by her weak ass attempt to be in my business because Shawn called pretty much immediately after. Of course.

"You really went on the internet with that bullshit? You're an idiot." Shawn said so eloquently as soon as I answered the phone.

"I'm a reflection of you, bitch!" I laughed. "I'm the idiot but you're so smart that you showed up to a party in LA like I wouldn't find out, when you knew I was out here?" My question was obviously rhetorical.

"That's why I don't trust your dumb ass now. Cus you always run your fucking mouth." Shawn spit back.

"I didn't even say your name, bitch. It's not my fault you're such a fuck boy that the whole internet knows your fuck boy ways off top. I hope the next bitch you fuck gives your ass an STD. You dirty dick ass nigga." I yelled.

I was starting to get more irritated and Shawn was silent on the other end of the phone.

And then he said, "Why the fuck is Marissa Jackson DM'ing me? Why the fuck would you tell her anything about me? And why the fuck…"

I cut him off. "I didn't tell her shit. That bitch hit MY phone talking about she saw us arguing at the party last night. She also told me I should use you for clout so I don't know why she would hit you on some buddy-buddy shit. Stop fucking playing with me." I said before I hung up in his face.

Naturally I wasn't going to let Shawn see how pissed I was that Marissa messaged him but I was ready to pull up on her and beat her ass for that bullshit. I didn't know exactly what she had said in her message to Shawn because I didn't give him the opportunity to tell me, so instead, I called my homegirl Ashley because her and Marissa were roommates. Ashley knew exactly why I was calling her and immediately told me how bad she felt that Marissa had reached out to Shawn. According to Ashley, Marissa told Shawn that I was trying to use him for clout and that shit set me off considering that is what she literally called me and told me to do. Doing shit for a come up was never me, everything I had flowed naturally to me. Not to mention, the way that she could blatantly lie was very fucking strange but the fact that Shawn would believe that bullshit was even more strange, so I called him back so that we could have another raggedy ass conversation.

Honestly, I didn't think he was going to answer since I hung up on him before but as soon as he did I said, "So your dumb ass really believed what that thirsty ass bitch said?" I paused.

I didn't give Shawn time to answer. "That dumb bitch called me to tell me that you and your brother are a good lick. She basically thinks the *Davis Brothers* are just a fucking come up and you want to fix your mouth to tell me that you don't trust *me*?" I laughed hysterically.

"You're the fucking problem, Shawn. You're so fucking stupid that you don't even know a real bitch when she's right in your fucking face. You worried about me telling my followers a story that didn't even have your name in it, meanwhile there's bitches trying to come up off you." I said.

Shawn finally spoke. "Shut the fuck up…"

I cut him off again, "No, bitch. You shut the fuck up. I hope the blogs eat you the fuck up. You're dead to me. Fuck you nigga." I said.

After that, I hung up on him and started crying. I was acting tough on the phone but that shit really broke my heart. It was like one thing after another was pulling us further and further apart from each other and I hated that. I didn't think there was a chance for us to bounce back from our argument at the party that night but I knew there wasn't a chance for us to bounce back from what had just happened. So that was that. Another heartbreak at the hands of a man I loved.

15

DANGEROUSLY IN LOVE

AS YOU COULD IMAGINE, after the whole story time on *Live* thing, plus Marissa trying to be on some sneaky shit and me and Shawn getting in that huge argument, I was mentally and emotionally exhausted. I probably stayed in bed for another hour that morning before I finally got up and hung out with Destinee in the living room. We talked briefly about what happened and how I felt, but you know I didn't share too much. I felt physically ill. Thankfully, my flight back to Atlanta was later that night, so I was making sure I held all of my emotions back until I was back at my apartment where I could process everything on my own time, in my own space.

Even though it probably would have been a good time to do so, I didn't use my flight home to write any new songs or get any work done, I just used it to sleep. I knew that since I was basically just going back to Atlanta to pack up all my stuff and move to LA, I wasn't going to have much time for sleep. Besides that, I didn't really know how depressed I'd become when it started to set in that Shawn and I were really done. Since I had gone through such a dark time due to lack of sleep before, I didn't want that to happen again. I could feel my heart breaking and I knew that it would turn ugly quickly if I didn't at least try to gain some control over my emotions. I know that so far I've painted Shawn out to be some narcissistic, manipulative, gaslighter, and he absolutely was, but in the moment I was thinking of the good times. It was all of our conversations, laughs and good sex we shared that bonded us together so closely. We really were a match made in heaven when we weren't being completely toxic towards each other. I think my heart was breaking even more for what could have been.

When I got back to Atlanta, I only had about a week to pack up the rest of my apartment and hire a moving company to move my stuff back across the world. With the way I was feeling, all I wanted to do was curl up with Orien and watch TV, but I forced myself to pack up my kitchen so that I could stay on schedule. I obviously had to leave a few things unpacked so that I could use them over the next week but ya girl was tired after packing just the kitchen. It took much longer than I expected and it was much more work than I intended for it to be so I knew that regardless of the fact that I had sent some stuff to LA already, the rest of my place was going to be a lot of work.

You would think that I would get super focused knowing that I barely had any time left to pack my entire apartment up but my head was still stuck on Shawn so I decided I needed a self-love day. I woke up early one morning, took a super hot shower, made myself some breakfast and then my first stop was the nail shop. After the nail shop, I went to the spa and got a full body massage, body detox treatment and a facial. It was the most relaxed and at peace I had been in what felt like forever. It was really a go-with-the-flow type of day and I ended up taking myself to lunch and then going shopping, as if I didn't already have too many clothes to pack up. I didn't care though because everything I had done that day really helped me take my mind off of the bullshit. I'm not saying that retail therapy is the right way to handle all of your problems but it definitely always helps me see the light at the end of the tunnel.

Listen, I'm never going to act like I know everything but it's obvious that I've been through a lot. Even if I haven't always gotten through my trauma in a way that you feel is the right way, I've always gotten through it. You know why? Because I do what's right for me without taking into consideration whether or not it looks or sounds right to anybody else. I mean, at this point in my life I've spent so much money on therapy that I could probably be your therapist. But back then, I had to get through the darkness how I saw best. So, if I can give you any form of unwarranted advice it would be to do what's best for you, no matter what it looks like to other people. Of course that is limited to not inflicting harm onto yourself or others, but if retail therapy is your thing, throw it in the bag, sis. If disappearing from your loved ones for a few days until you get your mind right is your thing, then lay low until you're ready to pop back out. If you are the type that just needs to take a nap, then catch your zzz's, girl. My point is that whatever YOU need to do to help yourself come out on the other side of trauma, do that. Reflect on the experience, reset after the pain and then raise your price in every single way.

Sorry, I didn't mean to get all deep and shit, I just want to make sure that I'm not telling you my story in vain. I want you to take the pieces of my life that resonate with you, and use them to help you grow. Anyway, when my self-love day was over, I went home, unwinded for a while and then started packing the rest of my apartment. I was looking forward to moving in with Destinee. I was looking forward to having her company around me whenever we were home at the same time. The thing I was looking forward to the most though, was another fresh start because if it's one thing I'm never afraid to do, it's start over.

BEFORE I KNEW IT, my apartment was finally packed up and all my stuff was loaded into the moving truck ready to head back to LA. Leaving Atlanta behind was a bittersweet feeling just the same way it was when I moved from LA to Atlanta, but this time I felt much more accomplished and even more mature. Atlanta was good to me. It gave me room to grow as a woman and it prepared me to grow my business and my brand even more than I had already done. I was ready to go back to LA so that I could conquer more goals and be surrounded by people that loved me. I was also ready to get back to LA to put all my energy into growing my music career. I had actually already set up a few studio sessions, planned on going to a listening party and had some meetings lined up. My plan was to touchdown in LA and get shit popping pretty much immediately because I still had some buzz going from my *Rolling Loud* show.

A WEEK later and I had finally made it to LA and gotten settled in my new spot but my car was going to take about three more days to get there. I wasn't really too pressed about it because Des had a car and I didn't mind taking *Uber* but I planned on trading my little *Kia* in for a *Mercedes* anyway. The *Kia* got me through some times in Atlanta but it was nothing like my *Audi*, plus it was time for me to level up again. I wanted a car that had rich bitch energy. The rest of my stuff was also going to take about three days to get to LA and that was a little more pressing for me since I already had events and studio sessions lined up. The listening party was first on the list, so you know me and Des had to hit the mall.

———

MY OUTFIT WAS SIMPLE: a white strapless dress that fit me like a glove, as per usual, and a cute pair of heels. My makeup and hair were always on point so I always knew I could get away with a simple outfit. The venue for the listening party was pretty small but it wasn't overcrowded like I expected it to be. There was a small stage that was giving very much DIY, but it worked for what the vibe of the venue was. Near the entrance there was a small bar so that's the first thing Destinee and I did when we walked in. After getting our drinks, we posted up midway between the bar and the stage so that we had a good view of the stage but easy access to the bar in case we needed more drinks to help us enjoy the music. Neither of us had heard of the artist that we were there to see but he was signed to a pretty big label, so it was a good look for me to be there so that I could network with some music execs.

Halfway through the listening party some guy ended up standing right next to me. His vibe was different. I don't think I've ever described anybody as eclectic before, but this guy was definitely eclectic. There was something different about him. The way he dressed and the way he looked was very artsy and I liked it. He must have felt me staring at him because he glanced over his left shoulder and smiled at me.

"Oh. My bad." He said. "I'm just all in your space. T. Stacks, how you doin'?" He said as he held his hand out so that I could shake it.

"Nah, you're good. I'm Winter. Nice to meet you." I shook his hand. "This is my best friend Destinee." I grabbed Destinee's hand.

T. Stacks and Destinee shook hands and then he quickly looked at me again.

"You heard his music before?" He asked me.

I looked over at the stage. "No, I haven't actually. This is my first time. I like him though. He's cool." I said.

"Yeah, nah, I fuck with him. I'm really into Asian rap, but this shit is a vibe. I fuck with it." He said before taking a sip of his drink.

I took a second to think about what name he used when he introduced himself. "What did you say your name was? I know you literally just told me. I'm the worst with names."

"You good." He laughed. "It's T. Stacks."

"Cute. What's the 'T' for?" I asked.

He laughed. "It's for Tony – well, Anthony. But nobody calls me that. You can just call me Stacks, it's easier."

"Ok. Cool. Well, nice to meet you, Stacks." I said.

By that time, we were listening to the last song of the night and even though I hadn't really had the chance to introduce myself to any music execs or any of the who's who of the label, I was ready to go. I had a long day of traveling, a long week of packing and a long list of secret emotions that I was still trying to process. Ya girl was tired as fuck. Luckily, Des has always been ready to leave whenever I am. I figured since we were leaving before the event was over, I would just tell Stacks that it was nice to meet him and then quietly leave without interrupting anything.

"Ok, Stacks. Well, it was nice to meet you." I basically whispered.

"Oh damn, you're out?" He said.

"Yeah, I just got in town. I'm hella jet lagged so I need to go to bed." I smiled.

"I feel that. Ok, here, take my number down. You're super chill, let's grab lunch or something." Stacks replied.

We exchanged numbers and then from that day forward,

we started spending crazy amounts of time together. It turned out that Stacks was actually a rapper himself, so he understood my busy studio schedule and enjoyed spending time with me during my sessions. Even though I fucked with Stacks, I wasn't allowing myself to get too deep into the situation because quite frankly, I still loved Shawn. My heart wasn't ready to love someone else and my mind wasn't ready to allow it.

Things were happening fast in my life. My car and all of my things had finally made it to LA, I was still trying to furnish my bedroom and bathroom, running my store, hosting events and in the studio heavy. Not to mention Stacks and I were spending almost every day together. We always had hella fun together. His energy and personality made me feel free – my inner child was always front and center whenever I was with him and that's what I appreciated most about our situation.

A few months in, I could feel Stacks' feelings for me grow deeper, so I tried to pull back just a little because I wasn't trying to feel responsible for him falling in love with me or anything like that. I started trying to spend less time with him by saying stuff like Destinee needed help with something or whatever other excuses I could come up with. It only worked for so long before one night he called me to tell me to get dressed because we were about to go party. Partying with him was always fun and it was usually less intimate so it was like cool, fuck it, I'll go.

When Stacks got to my house, he sent me a text message letting me know that he was outside and I told him to give me five minutes and I'd come out. I was in the middle of telling Destinee that I thought he was starting to fall in love with me and for whatever reason I wanted to finish telling her before I left. At first Des was campaigning for Stacks. She felt like he was a good match for me. She said that I seemed happy when I was around him and she loved that for me. She also felt as though I deserved to have a man that loved me more than I loved him. I wasn't trying to hear any of that though. I mean, I didn't tell her that of course, but I knew where my heart was and it wasn't with Stacks.

Somewhere between calling me to tell me that we were going to go out and me getting into the car, Stacks decided that we were just going to party at his house. I wasn't really feeling the change in plans but I was already dressed and ready to go so I didn't make it a big deal.

"We're going to link with Icon first." Stacks said as he kissed my neck.

"Ok. Where? Like are we getting food or something?" I said as I put my seatbelt on.

As he drove off he said, "Oh. Nah. He's in Hollywood. I just want to pick something up from him right quick and then we'll go back to my spot and get lit."

I didn't say anything. I assumed that he was probably about to pick some weed up from Icon because that was usually why they linked.

Long story short, we met up with Icon, Stacks got out of the car, they talked for a few minutes and then we were on our way to Stacks' house. On the way there, he had some Asian rap playing loud as hell as if we were in some sort of *Tokyo Drift* movie but that was Stacks. He was different.

When we finally got to his house, Stacks played the same music we were listening to in the car, on the surround sound speakers inside of his house as soon as we walked in. I'm not going to lie, I was sort of looking forward to going out and partying with him that night because we always got super turnt. The fact that we were at his house instead was a little annoying. Especially since I was trying to fall back a little anyway. I was prepared to make the best of the night though because he always had hella alcohol in his kitchen and that night was no different. The first thing I did was pour Stacks and I double shots of tequila.

"Salud!" He yelled. "To love, peace and great sex." He said before tapping his glass with mine.

"Cheers!" I said, making sure that I made eye contact with him.

We both downed our shots without chasers. Stacks threw his back like it was a small glass of water – I struggled a little with mine, but I got it done.

"Ok. We're trying something new tonight. You trust me?" Stacks said as he put his hand in his pocket.

"Aw fuck. Sure. I trust you. Do I need another shot first?" I joked.

Stacks smiled as if I had given him a million dollar idea. "Actually, yeah. Let's take two more."

In my head I was thinking t*wo?! Damn bitch I barely made it through the first one.*

Stacks poured two more shots for us and we took them back to back. The music was just as loud as it would have been if we were in the club so I was feeling like the night wasn't going to be so bad after all.

The next thing I knew, Stacks was tapping a small canister onto the counter and a white powder was coming out of it. My heart skipped a beat because I had never seen him do coke before. I didn't even know he was into that sort of thing but he appeared to be a professional coke cutter. He pulled out a credit card and started to tap through the powder, making two separate lines. I was speechless. In my head I was thinking like *damn, this nigga is about to snort two lines of coke at the same time?* 'Cus there was literally no way in hell he thought *I* was about to play with that shit.

He smiled at me and then walked over and hugged me from behind while he kissed on my neck. "Just do one line with me."

I pressed my body into his, hoping that it would ease him into what I was about to say because he had clearly lost his mind.

"I'm good. Let's just take more shots. We'll still have fun." I said, trying my best to sound sweet.

"Babe. Come on. Don't you trust me? You don't trust me, huh?" Stacks whined.

"It's not about trust. I just … I don't know. I'm just not into that." I replied.

"One line will barely do anything to you. If anything, it'll make you feel like you haven't taken any shots yet. Come on. Just one line. Trust me." He begged.

I'm not sure in what world you have to prove that you trust somebody by doing a line of coke, but Stacks was making me feel bad. I did trust him, I just didn't want to do coke to prove that I trusted him. Like, what the fuck?

"Stacks…" I started.

"Fuck it. You don't trust me. That's crazy. I really thought we were better than that." He was agitated.

I stood there for a moment, contemplating.

I was hesitant. "Alright. Fine. What do I need to do?"

Stacks smiled, pulled out a one hundred dollar bill and then rolled it up into a little nose straw. He walked me through what I had to do and what it would feel like as he demonstrated by doing a line himself. Before it was my turn, he poured more shots for us to take. Realistically I didn't need another shot but I was so scared to do coke that I felt like I needed the shot to help me get through it.

It felt like as soon as I snorted the coke up my nose, it went to my brain. It felt like an instant rush of adrenaline – like I could jump off a building and fly like a plane or something crazy. I was fucked up. It even seemed like the music had gotten louder. It seemed like watching me snort coke turned Stacks on. We started kissing and that led to us fucking right there on the kitchen counter. Somehow we ended up in his bedroom and we fucked there too. To say the least, it was a wild night filled with tequila and cocaine.

The next morning, I was surprised that I didn't feel hungover but I was filled with regret because obviously I had never done coke before and it wasn't something I had ever planned on doing either. Stacks seemed like he was happy – accomplished even. He was kissing on my back as I laid there pretending to have just woken up.

"You're so beautiful." He said.

I just smiled. I didn't really have too much to say.

He continued. "I need to tell you something."

I sat up. I feel like the worst thing you can say to some-body the morning after they do coke with you for the first time is that you need to tell them something. My anxiety was going crazy.

"I think I'm falling in love with you." He didn't even wait for me to ask him what he wanted to tell me.

My mind started racing. It was like I felt responsible for his feelings all of a sudden and that was exactly what I was trying to avoid.

"Stacks. You know I've been through so much." I said.

"I know. I don't expect you to say it back right now. This is how I feel though. The thing is that when I love people, it gets dark." He said as he caressed my face.

The last thing I've ever expected to hear anybody say to me is that their love is dark. I was confused because when shit got dark for me – it was a bad thing.

"What do you mean dark? What does that mean?" I asked.

"I don't really know how to explain it. I love hard. I love deep. Shit always gets very dark when I love and I don't know how to change that but I know that I'm falling for you." He explained.

"Well, I'm not really sure how to take that. I appreciate

your honesty, but I guess I just don't understand what that means." I paused. "Let's just take things slow and figure things out as we go." I said, hoping that he'd accept my response.

We had sex again that morning but my mind wasn't in it. I was so confused and disconnected. Afterwards, I took a hot shower and told Stacks that I had to get home so that I could get ready for a meeting. I didn't actually have a meeting but I didn't want to be stuck spending the entire day with him. It was starting to feel like a mistake to allow him to pick me up from my house instead of driving myself.

———

WHEN I GOT HOME, Destinee was already awake and watching TV in the living room.

She said, "Hey, sis. I didn't even know you were still out."

"Bitch. I have to cut Stacks off. If I told you about my night you would think I was nuts." I said as I plopped down next to her on the couch.

"Ok, well you won't believe what I found out last night." Destinee was almost excited.

Her statement had me ready to hear the tea – whatever it was.

"Oh? What's tea, sis?" I damn near yelled, forgetting about my Stacks struggle.

She unlocked her phone and started to scroll through it before she showed me a screenshot.

"Here, read and scroll. Read and scroll." Destinee said as she handed me her phone.

The screenshots she showed me were of multiple sources saying that Stacks had beat up his last girlfriend. There were screenshots of the girl's tweets, police reports, all types of shit. My heart fell to my stomach and I wanted to throw up.

If I had no other reason to leave Stacks alone, that was reason enough but I felt like I needed to ask him about it before just assuming that those reports were real.

"I need to ask him about this. What the hell?" I said as I handed Destinee her phone back.

"Man. I couldn't believe it when I saw it. I was really rooting for him last night but I take back everything I said. You were right. You definitely have to leave that nigga alone." Destinee said.

"Ok. I'm going to *FaceTime* him. Don't say anything. " I said.

My heart was pounding so hard and fast while I waited for Stacks to answer.

"Hey, I just got a DM from a fake page that has a bunch of screenshots talking about you putting your hands on your ex. I didn't reply or anything, but I do want to hear from you what happened." I made sure that my tone was as genuine as possible.

Stacks didn't seem to be bothered by what I said. "Oh, yeah. That wasn't that big of a deal. You know blogs and shit blow shit out of proportion. Me and my ex were toxic, so we were always putting our hands on each other but not anything crazy. She was just mad so she started posting shit and the blogs blew it up."

I heard him, but I didn't approve. "Oh. Ok. That makes sense. Ok, well I have to get ready for this meeting, I just wanted to ask you about that real quick." I rushed.

We got off the phone.

Destinee and I were both confused on whether or not he was telling the truth. I mean, Destinee didn't see his body language but I did and he wasn't defensive or anything. He was calm which made me believe he was being honest. The thing was that because of my past and the abuse that I had experienced, I couldn't get down with even a mutual fight where a man puts his hands on a woman. That was the moment I decided that I was definitely going to fall back because a domestic violence case mixed with telling me shit gets dark when you're in love was way too much for me. Plus, how do you sit there with a straight face and tell me that you and your ex putting your hands on each other wasn't a big deal? The red flags were in my face and I wasn't going to ignore them.

I THOUGHT it would be hard to fall back, but Stacks seemed to have fallen back a little too, which made it even easier. For the next few weeks, we hardly spoke to each other and we didn't see each other in person at all. Then boom, a few months passed and Stacks had a whole girlfriend. He was posting her all over his social media and I loved that for him because it meant that I was completely off the hook. Unfortunately, about six months after that, Destinee woke me up to some devastating news.

"Bitch. Are you ok? How do you feel?" Destinee said as she walked into my room.

"Well, I was sleeping good until you woke me up." I said, half asleep.

"No. I'm not talking about that. You didn't see it yet?" Destinee's tone was serious.

I was confused. "See what?" I asked.

"Stacks." She said.

"What about him?" I sat up.

Des took a deep breath and walked over to my bed. "It's bad, sis." She handed me her phone.

Rapper T. Stacks Dead in Apparent Murder-Suicide, the headline said.

My eyes filled up with tears and my heart felt like it stopped beating for a minute.

"What the fuck?" I said. "No. No. No." I continued and handed Destinee back her phone.

She took a look at her phone and must have realized that I didn't read the entire article but I was looking for my phone. I'm not sure why – I think I just needed to look at his social media or something.

"This is crazy. He killed his girlfriend and then he shot himself." Destinee said.

I was completely shocked. "What?!"

I guess I assumed someone had killed him and then themself.

Destinee was trying to choose her words carefully. "Her kids were there too. Some reports are saying they saw it happen but other ones are saying they were just in the house, so I'm not sure. I just know that her kids were for sure there."

Stacks' voice saying, *I love hard. I love deep. Shit always gets very dark when I love*, played in my mind.

Destinee continued talking but I couldn't hear anything coming from her mouth. My mind was racing. I couldn't believe it. My heart ached for that woman, her children, her family – everybody. I hated to feel grateful that I didn't stay. I hated telling myself *that could have been me*.

I was speechless.

16

DÉJÀ VU

IT WOULD BE a stretch to say that I "lost" Stacks because he was never mine in the first place. However, it didn't make a difference because learning about him dying and taking the life of someone who he claimed to have loved, sent me through a wide range of emotions very similar to what I felt when Cinco passed away. I mean it's hard processing the death of somebody who could be so evil, but a part of you mourns for the person you once knew and loved. So, with that, amongst other things, I was really fighting to keep myself from falling back into depression after T. Stacks died. I couldn't bring myself to go to his funeral. On one hand, it felt like showing up would have been the right thing to do but on the other hand, being that I'm a victim of domestic violence, it felt insensitive to the victim and her family so I just stayed away from it all together.

There was a point in time where you couldn't have paid me to believe that Destinee and I would ever be friends again but I was grateful that we were living together because I really don't think that I could have been alone while I processed that whole situation. Even though I didn't share my pain with her, being able to go home every night knowing that I wasn't alone was enough to help me push through my emotions. I started hosting more events, drinking a lot more, writing and recording more and putting all of the time and energy that I had left into *Frost* just so that I could keep my mind occupied. I knew first hand that an idle mind could become a dangerous place for me and I couldn't afford to be so depressed that I lost sleep, became suicidal and lost my mind again. Not when I was splitting the larger portion of four thousand dollar rent with Destinee and not for my future self either. Looking back, besides the fact that I had started drinking a lot more, I'm proud of how I navigated my emotions during that time. Sometimes it feels easier to crawl into a dark hole and pretend your struggles don't exist than it is to face them and keep pushing through. I'm happy I allowed myself to go through the emotions in order to heal.

It took me about two months to completely bounce back before I started to feel like myself again. The crazy thing was that I didn't even realize that I wasn't myself until I felt like me again. It was like I could breathe again and there wasn't a black cloud hovering over me every damn day. Funny enough, right around the time I started to feel normal again, I randomly got a text from Kevin Campos telling me that he was in LA for the summer and wanted to link. Outside of the issues that we had when we were dealing with each other, Kevin and I had such a dope bond as friends that I was completely down to spend some time with him. It didn't even have to be on no sneaky link type vibes because I knew that we could just chill on some homie shit and still catch a vibe. It did however have to be a sneaky link away from Destinee since her weirdo behavior with Kevin was the reason we stopped fucking with each other in the past.

It wasn't like I was concerned about Destinee and Kevin

reuniting their friendship or anything like that, I just wanted to avoid any beef between Destinee and I. Truth be told, Kevin wasn't the first nigga Des had done some weird shit behind. She low key always did some sus shit when it came to men so it just made the most sense to keep that away from her. Plus, I couldn't link with Kevin right away anyway because I was locked in – staying focused and perfecting my craft. I just knew that whenever I did link with him, I was not going to tell Destinee about it.

A few days later, I finally had a night off so I decided that I would make dinner for me and Des. It was a Friday night and I could have linked with Kevin or went to the club or something, but I honestly just wanted to chill and I figured Des would be down. Dinner was almost done when Destinee came out of her room.

"It smells bomb." She said as she stood in the doorway of the kitchen. "Can you save some for me? I'm about to go out with my homegirls but I definitely want a plate when I come back."

Not going to lie, she caught me off guard. "Oh." I was a little confused. "My bad. I didn't know you were going out. Ok. Bet. I'll save you a plate."

For as long as I can remember and whenever we were actually on good terms, Destinee didn't ever go outside without at least inviting me to go with her. We damn near did everything together, had our locations shared with each other again, and always checked on each other throughout the day while she was at work. So, the fact that I wasn't invited to chill with her and whatever friends she was going with was definitely weird but I didn't think too much about it. It was one of those things where I made a mental note without really understanding why I made it at the time. Anyway, when it was time for her to leave, we said our I love you's, I told her to be safe and have fun and she told me she'd text me when she was on her way back home.

Orien and I watched a movie, I cleaned the kitchen and then took a bubble bath while Destinee was gone. It was a pretty normal night until I finally got in bed and my intuition started tingling. You know a woman's intuition doesn't lie about shit. I couldn't figure out if the feeling was rational or irrational anxiety so I tried my best to just ignore it. That only lasted for maybe twenty minutes and then something told me that I should check Destinee's location, so I did. She was at a hookah spot in Hollywood, which was also very fucking normal so I just knew I was trippin' and needed to take my ass to sleep. I knew that the last couple of months had been a lot on me emotionally and that night was probably the first night where I was just relaxing without intentionally trying to occupy my mind from painfully intrusive thoughts so I figured depression was trying to catch up with me.

At some point, I had fallen asleep but woke up again at five o'clock in the morning. The first thing I realized was that I never heard Destinee come into the house. My body was tired and I wasn't trying to get out of bed just to go see if she made it home safely, so instead, I checked her location thinking that it was going to show me that she was home. Wrong. She was at some random house in Beverly Hills which was a little odd but I figured maybe she ended up going to a party.

My heart started to pound hard and fast like I had just ran a marathon. I couldn't tell why, but I was super anxious. Destinee was never the type to stay out all night – especially if she wasn't with me. I couldn't think of any reason she would be in Beverly Hills at five o'clock in the morning so I called her just to make sure everything was good but she didn't answer. Immediately after, I sent her a text that said, *are you good?* I was anxious, concerned, confused – I was a lot of things all at once.

Finally, later that morning, she texted me back with, *yeah, sorry. I'm good.* On one hand, I felt better knowing that she was safe but on the other hand, I wasn't really sure if I was really texting her or not because like, why wouldn't she have just called me back? You know?

She went on to tell me that she had gotten super drunk the night before so she ended up sleeping at her sister's house, (who by the way I know didn't live in Beverly Hills, which was weird but again, I didn't put too much on it) and thought that she had alcohol poisoning so she was going to go to the ER. Obviously that shit had me spooked so I was trying to figure out which hospital she was going to go to so that I could meet her there but she insisted that her sister was going to take her. She told me that she'd keep me posted and let me know when she was on her way back home. Now, thinking back on all of this, that wasn't a conversation that we would have ever had in text messages under any normal circumstance and I probably should have called her again or told her to call me, but I didn't – even though my intuition was still feeling very weird.

For the next few hours, my mind raced and my heart sat in the pit of my stomach because I was worried about my best friend. Destinee had a tendency of getting blackout drunk, so the fact that she had alcohol poisoning wasn't shocking but it was still bad. I was happy to know that she was with her sister because who knows what could have happened to her if she wasn't. I sat on the couch and scrolled aimlessly through all of my social media accounts while I waited for her to text me to tell me that she was on her way home. I was sitting there like a concerned mom.

I must have dozed off because the sound of Destinee's key unlocking the front door made me jump out of my sleep. I knew that it was Des so I jumped up off of the couch and unlocked the door from the inside.

"Finally, bitch!" I said as I opened the front door and gave Destinee a hug. "I don't know who told your ass to go out unsupervised."

We stopped hugging so that Destinee could actually make it all the way inside of the apartment. I closed the door and locked it behind her.

Destinee laughed. "Girl. You don't even fucking know. It's *Pedialyte* and *Advil* for the rest of the fucking day for me. I'm never drinking again." She said as we walked toward the couch.

As I sat down I asked, "What the fuck happened?"

"Honestly, I don't even remember. First we went to hookah, then we went to the club and the next thing I know – I was waking up at my sister's house and the whole fucking room was spinning." Destinee said as she laid her head down on the arm of the couch.

I went to the kitchen to pour her a glass of water, grab some crackers and get a trash bag in case she needed to throw up. Overall, she probably had two sips of the water, didn't touch the crackers and thankfully didn't use the trash bag at all. Instead, she slept in the same spot for the entire day while I sat on the other end of the couch. I ended up ordering pizza so that she would have something greasy to eat when she woke up. Of course, when she finally woke up, I had to damn near force her to eat a couple slices of pizza so that she could take an *Advil*. After that, I made her shower, down the bottle of *Pedialyte* and get in her bed so that she could sleep the rest of her hangover away. I was hoping she would be feeling better by the next day so that we could go out for a friend's birthday.

UNFORTUNATELY, for the next two weeks, Destinee was dead ass serious about not drinking again. We didn't do any type of turn up and she refused to go anywhere other than work for those two weeks. I mean, I was still living my life, I just didn't think she was serious about the whole no drinking thing because she wasn't green to blacking out or being hungover. Of course she wasn't used to the whole alcohol poisoning thing but like, bitch, you play stupid games, you win stupid prizes so I wanted her to chalk that shit up to an L and turn up with me!

Destinee wasn't trying to do shit, but Kevin had hit me again telling me that he was still in LA and wanted to make sure we linked before he left town. He happened to hit me on a night that I didn't have anything planned so I was like fuck it, come pick me up. Even though the plan was always not to tell Destinee that I was going to link with Kevin, the timing was perfect since she basically put herself on house arrest. Kevin and I were just going to grab dinner and catch up anyway, so I didn't really feel too bad leaving Des at the house. I threw on a pair of blue jeans, a white crop top and a pair of *Dior* sandals with my hair in a sleek, low bun with a middle part. It was giving very cute, casual and unassuming.

"I'm 'bout to go eat. I'll be back in a little bit." I said to Destinee before I walked out of the door.

She didn't even ask any questions, thankfully. "Love you!" She said as I closed the door.

I was low key excited to see Kevin because I knew that our friendship would basically pick up right where it left off before he decided to make that whole ass song about me. Shit like that becomes trivial after a while because our friendship held so much more weight than all of the emotional stuff did. When I got into his car, I could tell that he was just as happy to see me as I was to see him. We gave each other that awkward front seat side hug and then made our way to *Bossa Nova* for a quick dinner. We weren't trying to be seen, we weren't trying to do too much and we weren't trying to see anybody we knew because we were really just trying to vibe and catch up on all the things we had missed in each other's lives during the time we spent apart. It was a very platonic link up but the sexual chemistry was definitely still there.

By the time we made it to *Bossa Nova* and sat down at our table, we had gotten through most of Kevin's life updates. He was working on new music, deciding how he was going to expand his brand, stack money and continue enjoying life. I loved that for him. That was something I always really loved about him – his hustle. I updated him on everything I had been dealing with but I left out the whole Shawn era. Kevin and I were good friends but I didn't see a need to tell him about how in love I was with another man. All in all, it was clear that our friendship outlasted the test of time and distance.

After we talked about our lives and waited for our food, Kevin asked, "Oh, how's your homegirl doing?"

"Who – Destinee?" I mean, Kevin has met a few of my homegirls before so I genuinely didn't know which one he was asking about.

"Yeah, she was on some weirdo shit a couple weeks ago." Kevin casually replied.

At that point, he had my undivided attention. "A couple weeks ago when? What do you mean?" I asked – confused as hell.

Kevin was obviously shocked that I didn't know what he was talking about. "She didn't tell you? It was like two weeks ago or some shit. Shit, I thought you were going to pull up. Me and my boys had a table at some club, I don't even know what the name of it was. But one of my boys invited his lil sneaky link and she brought her girls with her. So when I saw Destinee, I said what's up to her but she was being weird."

I cut him off. "Weird like how though?"

"At first it was stupid shit. Like she kept saying *oh, you're speaking to me?*, when I said what's up to her. Which was dumb because I clearly spoke to her. Then as the night went on, I asked her if you were going to pull up. I mean shit, I ain't never seen her outside without you and I figured if she knew I was going to be there, you had to have known too." Kevin said.

I laughed sarcastically. "You would think. I literally had no idea, though."

"Ok, so yeah." Kevin processed what I had said. "So when I asked about you, she started saying shit like *oh, so I'm not good enough for you? Winter just has to be here, huh?*" Kevin paused and started laughing. "I don't know, bro. The shit was just really fucking weird and I just started keeping my distance because like I said, she was there with my nigga's girl. Anyway, we all end up going back to the house. We chillin', smokin', eatin' – whatever just vibin' out, you feel me?" He continued.

"Right." I said to let him know that I was still listening.

"So then, I don't know what the fuck happened or why but Shorty started acting super nutty. We was all turnt, but she was on some other shit. I don't know if she popped a pill or what the fuck was going on but she was on one. It was weird. Then it was like four of us standing in the kitchen and out of nofuckingwhere, she started taking her clothes off. Like butt-booty-ass naked." Kevin laughed.

I was in complete shock.

Kevin didn't let my shock stop him from spilling the tea. "So this bitch is butt naked in the middle of my kitchen, drunk as fuck, bent over, hands on her ankles talking about some stick it in, Kevin. Fuck me. Fuck me, Kevin. Are you going to stick it in?"

I gasped louder than I intended to and then I leaned in closer to Kevin and whispered. "Shut the fuck up. Say swear." I said.

Kevin was laughing even harder by then. "Nigga. I swear. She was FRIED. I was low key scared to react but I grabbed her elbow and like led her to the couch and told her to lay down. I was trying to be as nice and gentle as possible because that shit was so weird and I wasn't trying to deal with no type of bullshit behind her drunk ass."

"What the fuck." I chimed in.

"Nigga. WILD, right?" He laughed. "So when she finally laid down on the couch, I told the homies that were in the kitchen like yo, do not fucking touch her and then I sent that shit in a group chat too just to make sure everybody in the house knew that Shorty was trippin'. Hold on, let me find it." He started scrolling through his phone.

My blood was damn near boiling but I was trying my best not to explode.

"Look." Kevin showed me a text thread.

There's a girl on the couch by the kitchen DO NOT TOUCH HER. DO NOT FUCK HER. DO NOT TALK TO HER. We will definitely catch a case. DO NOT TOUCH HER! The text read.

That text was followed by at least five different variations of 'bet', by everyone in the group chat.

Even before seeing the text messages, I believed everything Kevin was telling me because for one, he had no reason to lie and two, it was all right on brand with who I knew Destinee to be. Actually seeing the texts made it that much more real, though. I had second hand embarrassment for her because like bitch, how are you so thirsty *and* sloppy. Pick a fucking struggle. I kept it cute so that Kev wouldn't see how mad I was though.

"This is so crazy to me." I said after reading the text messages.

I leaned back in my chair, folding my arms across my chest. "So did she leave like shit was sweet the next morning? Or what was the finale of this shit show?" I asked.

Kevin was shocked. "Nigga. What? It's so sick that you really don't know anything about that night. This bitch threw up all over my bathroom floor, didn't tell anybody that she did and left before anybody was even awake."

"Are you fucking kidding me?!" I damn near yelled. I realized that I was loud, so I repeated myself but in a whisper. "Are you fucking kidding me?"

"Swear. When we were at the club the night before she had kept pressing me for my number and at first I kept saying no but eventually I gave it to her and she called my phone so that I had hers. So when I woke up the next day and saw that she had thrown up all over the bathroom I called her and made her come back to the crib to clean that shit up." He said.

"This is so embarrassing." I shook my head.

"Nah. It was really crazy. Like I couldn't believe any of that shit was going down. She was never like that back in the day so I was dumb confused. I mean, I'm sure she was embarrassed too but like damn. Shorty definitely has to slow down on the liquor or the pills or whatever the fuck she had goin' on that night."

Luckily, our food had just been brought to the table and it was perfect timing because I had no words. I wanted to leave the restaurant and go home to press my issue with Des right then and there, but it just wasn't the right time. Kevin and I changed the subject, ate our dinner, enjoyed each other's company and then we ended up going back to his place. That wasn't the plan when I had him pick me up but it was probably what was best for both me and Destinee because with the way I was feeling, I was liable to do anything.

What she did felt deliberately disrespectful to me. Like, yeah, I know the bitch gets blackout drunk on a regular basis but she intentionally went out without me that night. She had never once gone out without inviting me even if she knew that I couldn't make it or wouldn't want to go. She never really even told me what her plans were for the night, which was also not like her at all. So, I could only assume that she knew well before going out that night that she was going to see Kevin, which was why she didn't ask me if I wanted to go. Without even knowing it, Kevin had exposed all of Destinee's lies from that night. She said that she was at her sister's house when she finally texted me back but the truth was that she was at Kevin's house cleaning her throw up off of his bathroom floor. Who knows if she actually ever slept at her sister's house. She obviously never went to the ER and probably didn't have alcohol poisoning either. I couldn't believe I was up all night worried about her dumb ass, and I was furious that she would lie about her health just to cover up the truth.

17

TWO ROUNDS

CATCHING up and unexpectedly spending the night with Kevin for the was cool but I couldn't stop thinking about how mad I was at Destinee. After we had breakfast, Kevin offered to take me home but I had already texted my homegirl telling her to pick me up from his place so that she could be with me when I confronted Destinee. The fact that two weeks had gone by and Destinee hadn't mentioned not one single thing about the full production she put on for Kevin had me feeling like there was no telling how she would react when I pressed her about it. Not only that, but she blatantly lied to me which was probably what had me the most mad, so I just felt like it was better if I had a friend with me that could intervene if shit got too crazy.

When we got to my place, Destinee was sitting on the couch watching TV.

"Hey, sis." She said when I walked through the door.

When she realized my homegirl was with me she said, "Hey girl hey."

My homegirl spoke to Destinee, but I didn't say a word. I sat on the couch while my homegirl walked to my room because when we were on the way to my place, we both decided that it would be better for her to chill in my room unless it sounded like shit was going to pop off. I didn't want Destinee to feel attacked or bombarded. I just couldn't let what she did slide.

I don't even remember what Des was watching on TV but she was super into it and I hadn't really decided how I wanted to approach the situation so for about five minutes, I just sat there next to her pretending to watch whatever she was watching.

Finally, I decided to give her the opportunity to tell me the truth. "Des." I took a deep breath. "Is there anything you need to tell me?" I asked calmly.

She looked over at me with a smirk on her face and confusion in her eyebrows. "No."

I'm not even going to lie – I was offended. Anybody that knows me, knows that if I'm asking a question like that, it's because I already know the answer.

I scratched my eyebrow. "There's absolutely nothing you think I should know?" That time, there was a little more irritation in my voice because she low key had me fucked up.

Destinee matched my irritation with an attitude of her own. "I said no."

The audacity to have an attitude with me while you're lying to my face about some weak ass shit that you did is wild but for some reason, I still gave her ass another opportunity to answer the question.

"So, you don't need to tell me shit about Kevin, Destinee? Nothing at all?" At that point, I had an attitude too.

Destinee was defensive. "No. I don't owe you shit. Don't gotta tell you shit. Not telling you shit. The fuck?"

Honestly, my feelings were hurt more than anything at that moment.

I snapped. "You're so fucking grimey, Des. I've literally

done *everything* for you. When I get clothes – I'm getting *us* clothes. When you can't hold up your end of the bills, I'm the one that busts that shit down for you – no questions asked, even though I'm already paying more rent than you. I've put every apartment we've had in *my* name. I'm ready to ride for you whether you're right or wrong. I ain't never crossed you for no nigga. Ever. I have been nothing but loyal to you but that shit is dead! I don't care how you make it happen, but you need to start paying half the fucking bills. You keep playing in my face like that shit is cute and it's not. So ain't no more loyalty. You figure your shit out however you need to because I'm not helping you with shit else." I yelled.

My heart was racing, my palms were clammy and I could feel a lump forming in the back of my throat. I was so angry that I wanted to cry but I wasn't about to give her that satisfaction so after I said what I had to say, I stood up so that I could walk to my room. Destinee must have assumed that I was standing up to fight her because she stood up too. When she stood up, it only took me a split second to make the decision to fire on her first. It wasn't what I wanted but it was what had to happen because either she was going to swing first or I was. I'm not proud to say it, but I was beating the shit out of Des. It was like we went from best friends to enemies and all of my anger surfaced immediately after I took that first swing. At some point my homegirl came out of my bedroom and broke the fight up.

Destinee had blood all over her face. My carpet had her blood all over it. The couch had drops of blood on it too. It was a bloody fucking mess. I really couldn't believe that it came to that but I didn't feel no type of way about it. My homegirl stood in between Destinee and I as she led me toward the front door.

"Let's go. Come on. Let's just leave, Winter. Sleep at my house tonight. Let's just leave." My homegirl said.

Destinee didn't say a word and neither did I. I didn't even think to wash my hands or pack any clothes – I just left. It wasn't until I was in the car on the way to my homegirls house that it really hit me that I had just beat the shit out of my best friend. My feelings were hurt but I felt like she deserved it. How many times am I supposed to let a bitch play in my face about a nigga? That shit is weird and unnecessary. It was a good thing I decided to have my homegirl with me because ain't no tellin' how much worse that situation would have been if she wasn't there to break us up.

My hands were sore and my knuckles were bruised by the time we pulled up at my homegirls house. I had to replay my conversation with Kevin in my mind and remind myself that it wasn't the first time Destinee had done weird shit like that. I had to decide what I would do next if Destinee decided that she would no longer be my roommate since I beat her ass. Shit, I had to decide if I really wanted to be her roommate after all of that shit too. All that thinking and I didn't have one answer. As a matter of fact, the entire rest of that day is still a blur to me.

The next morning, the only thing on my mind was avoiding more conflict with Destinee. I wanted to go home but I wasn't really trying to deal with any of the bullshit that could have come after a fight like the one we had since she was still my whole ass roommate. As far as I was concerned, she was no longer a friend to me but I didn't care if she continued to live in the apartment because I had already told her that she was about to start paying half the bills instead of the way less than half that she was paying. In my mind, the only thing that remained of our friendship was the fact that our locations were still shared with each other and that worked in my favor because I was able to check her location that morning to see that she was at work. Of course we'd have to cross paths at some point, but I was glad to know that she was at work so that I could just go home and go to my room without having to walk through the awkward energy in the house. In my mind, the worst had already happened – I beat Destinee up.

Since she wasn't home, I didn't need my friend to take me home. I took an *Uber* instead so that I could just have a minute to myself. When I got there, I opened the front door only to realize that Destinee's sister was sitting on my couch watching TV. In all the time that me and Des lived in that apartment, her sister had never been there so it was real fucking strange that she was sitting on my couch all of a sudden.

"Wassup? Where is Destinee?" I asked in confusion.

Listen, I may have done some stupid shit in my life, but I've never been a fool. I knew that Destinee's sister had to be in my house on some weird shit but I was once again trying to give a bitch the benefit of the doubt.

Destinee's sister very calmly said, "I don't know."

"Where is Destinee?" I was getting irritated so I repeated my question.

Destinee's sister didn't have any type of emotion in her voice. "I don't know where she is."

It was real fucking weird so I just rolled my eyes, walked to my room and locked my door. I knew something was off but I couldn't figure out what it was because Destinee's location was still showing that she was at work and if her sister was there to fight me, I felt like she would have done it as soon as I walked in the door. For a while, I just stayed in my room contemplating what I should do and then I decided to change my clothes. Basically, I was getting ready to fight again. Even though I couldn't figure out the angle, I was one thousand percent sure that Destinee's sister was sitting in my house so that she could get her lick back on behalf of Destinee. My hair was already in a bun but I threw on some sweats and prepared myself to step back into the living room so that I could ask Destinee's sister what she was in my house for.

I probably stepped out of my room and made it all of five steps toward the living room before I heard Destinee's bedroom door open. Obviously I wasn't thinking about this at the time, but she intentionally left her phone at work so that I wouldn't know that she was home. That little piece of information makes this next part super embarrassing for her.

Destinee tried to sneak me. She ran up from the side without saying anything and we got to fighting and ended up in the kitchen where I slammed her onto the ground. After that, I had control of the situation and I beat her ass all over that fucking kitchen. Blood was splattering everywhere again just like it did the day before but this time it was from a big ass scratch she made on my shoulder. I hated having to do her like that because she was really my best friend but she wanted the round two so she got it.

I pinned her down to the floor with my body and started yelling at the top of my lungs. "You did this shit to yourself! Look at you! Look at what you did!"

By that point, her sister came into the kitchen and pulled me off of Destinee but that didn't stop me from screaming at her.

"I treated you like a fucking sister, bitch!" I was fighting back tears as I screamed at her. "I did everything for you! Everything I do was always for US! I always made sure your sorry ass was good! I never asked you for shit and this is what you give me! You were my fucking sister!" I screamed as Destinee's sister pushed me further away from Destinee.

Destinee backed as far away from me as she could and she started crying. "I'm sorry. I'm fucking sorry! I was embarrassed. I fucked up and I was embarrassed. I was so fucking drunk I didn't even know what the hell I was doing and that's so embarrassing!" She cried even harder.

"Then you should've fucking said that!" I yelled with no remorse whatsoever. "Now we been in here fighting for two days straight and for what?! For what, Destinee? Because you were too fucking embarrassed to keep it real?"

Destinee's sister was standing halfway between Destinee and I. After she separated us, she said, "She right, D. You deadass wrong for that."

I was shocked to hear that because I honestly thought she was there to fight me and when Des tried to sneak me, I thought they were going to jump me. The last thing I ever expected was to hear Destinee's sister agreeing with me after I just beat her sister up a second time within twenty-four hours.

"That shit was foul, D and you know it." Destinee's sister said.

Des didn't say anything but she was crying even harder than she was before.

Of course I felt bad for her dumb ass so I started crying too.

"This friendship is dead, Destinee. Pay half the bills or let me know if you're moving out." I said as I walked to my bedroom. "This shit is dumb."

The rent alone was four thousand dollars and I knew that realistically, Destinee couldn't afford to pay anymore than what she was already paying but it was no longer my responsibility to help her figure shit out. Her apology came too late. I knew that paying all of the bills on my own was going to be annoying but I didn't care whether she stayed or left.

THE NEXT WEEK was so awkward. We both stayed in our rooms most of the time unless we were in the kitchen for something but it was one of those things where if she knew I was in the kitchen, she would wait until I went back into my room and vice versa. Believe it or not, that expensive ass apartment only had one bathroom so we would also have to awkwardly pay attention to if the other person was in there or not when we needed to shower or whatever.

Things got super weird when I came home one day and Destinee had her auntie and her sister helping her pack her shit up. We never had any type of conversation about whether she was going to stay or go and we definitely didn't discuss the fact that she would be leaving so soon without any type of notice. It was yet another inconsiderate move on Destinee's part but very on brand for who she was. Of course I was pissed off but it was like, what was I going to do, beat her ass for a third time? Nah. I didn't say a word to Destinee, her auntie or her sister. Instead, I quietly went into my room, closed my door and sent a text to all of my homegirls to let them know that I was looking for a new roommate. No one even bothered to ask for details because when Destinee and I moved in with each other again, all my girls already knew it was a shit show waiting to happen. I guess I should've listened to them.

18

ALL THAT GLITTERS AIN'T GOLD

THIS MIGHT SOUND crazy but I didn't expect Destinee to move out after we got into it. Like, I know getting your ass beat is embarrassing – especially if it happens twice within a twenty-four hour span, but I just felt like it was one of those things where we catch the fade, go through a couple weeks of awkwardness and then move on without ever mentioning it again. Of course our friendship was never going to be the same after all of that, but I just didn't really think she was going to actually move out. It didn't bother me that she did, I just wasn't really expecting it. Unfortunately, none of my homegirls knew of anybody looking for a roommate at the time, so I had to pay the entire four-thousand dollars for rent the following month on my own. Luckily, I was able to do that but I was for damn sure not trying to do that shit every month. Especially when I was just paying for an empty room to sit there.

Right before it was time to pay the full rent on my own for the second month in a row, I ended up hosting a party and taking my girls with me. This particular promoter wanted me to bring more girls than I normally brought out with me, so I had my homegirls invite some of their friends too. Normally, I wouldn't have too many girls come out with me because it starts to get messy but I needed to host that event because I wanted to make sure that I was able to maintain my lifestyle and keep up with the extra rent and utilities I had to pay for since Destinee was gone. I mean I wasn't pressed for money but I definitely had to move differently than I did when I was only paying a portion of the rent. A friend of mine ended up inviting a girl that she knew. From my understanding, they weren't like friends, friends – they just partied together. The girl's name was Jasmine. She was a pretty chunky Asian-looking girl – probably mixed with something else too because she didn't look full Asian.

At some point during the party, Jasmine introduced herself to me.

She was hella cheerful. "Hi, I'm Jasmine. Tash told me you were looking for a roomie!"

"Oh, yeah. I am, actually. You look hella young though. How old are you?" I asked.

"I'm twenty-one." She said with a smile.

"Oh dope. Cool. Where do you live right now?" I yelled over the loud music.

"I'm in San Diego right now. That's where I'm from. But I'm trying to move to LA ASAP." Jasmine yelled back.

I definitely needed a roommate, but I wasn't desperate for one, so I wanted to talk with Jasmine a little more before I just told her she could move into my house.

"Ok. Well, take my number down. We can talk tomorrow morning." I yelled.

Jasmine gave me her phone and I dialed my number so that I could call my phone from hers. From what I could tell, she seemed pretty cool that night. She was definitely a young bitch, but she held her liquor well, got along with everyone at my table and didn't seem like she was a problematic type of girl. My only concern was whether or not she was really going to be able to afford to live with me. Her half of the rent was going to be two-thousand dollars plus half of the utilities each month on top of whatever else she had to pay for every month. I was looking forward to talking to her about everything but I for sure wasn't getting my hopes up.

THE NEXT MORNING, at about ten o'clock, I had a text from Jasmine that said, *hey, have a second to talk?*

Normally, I like to have my mornings to myself but I appreciated Jasmine's assertiveness so I texted her back letting her know that she could call right then if she was ready. Sure enough, she did.

"Hey, girl. I just wanted to tap in with you about the roommate situation 'cus I'm definitely serious about it." Jasmine got right into it.

"Oh, yeah, no, for sure. Well, let me just tell you how much rent is off top so that you know if this is even something you want to do. I'm not doing background checks or anything, so you would have to put down a full month's rent as your deposit – which is four thousand and then your half of the rent each month will be two thousand. So basically you'd have to pay six up front and then two every month plus utilities which is only like three to four hundred a month." I was nice but stern.

I knew that paying six thousand up front sounded crazy as fuck but I had to protect myself. You already know that I've been fucked over by way too many roommates and those were bitches I actually knew. I didn't know Jasmine from a bitch off the street so I had to do what I had to do – period.

Jasmine wasn't phased by what I had said. "That's fine.

You want cash or do you want me to get a money order or something?"

I was low key kind of shocked. "Cash will be fine. Ok, cool. So since that works for you – let me just ask you a few questions to see if we would even be a good fit for living with each other. I just don't want to waste your time or mine. You know?"

Jasmine was a super nice girl. "Oh, I'm not trippin' at all."

"What do you do for work." I asked.

"I'm a webcam girl. So I'll mostly be in my room all day because that's how I pay my bills." She said with confidence.

I'm not going to lie, I definitely didn't expect the little bitch to tell me she was a webcam girl but I didn't give a damn. Like, girl, as long as you'll be on time with your bill money every month, go ahead and play with your pussy all day.

"Perfect. Ok, I'm not trying to be in your business, but do you have a man?" I asked without skipping a beat.

Jasmine laughed a little. "Yeah, I do. But he's in jail. He's supposed to get out in a few months, but I'm not really sure."

Another piece of information I wasn't ready for but didn't care about because if her nigga was in jail, that meant he would't be walking around my house all the time. The last thing I wanted was a roommate who had a nigga that damn near lived with us too.

"Got it. Ok, well, I know it's only like a week away, but if you can have the money together on the first, then you can move in then." I said.

"That's perfect. Yeah. I already have it so that works for me. You're in North Hollywood, right? I think that's what Tash told me." Jasmine sounded excited.

"Yeah, I am. I don't know if you want to drive all the way out here, but you're more than welcome to come look at it this week if you want." I offered.

She said, "I actually won't have time because of work and packing and stuff. Could you just send me pictures of everything?"

"Yup. I'll do that right now." I said as I got out of bed.

"Cool. Thank you so much. I'm excited." Jasmine said.

"No, thank you. See you soon." I said.

We hung up the phone. Even though everything sounded good, I was a little nervous. I had never really lived with a complete stranger before. Like, yeah, my homegirl partied with her, but she didn't even know enough to tell me that Jasmine was a webcam girl or that her nigga was in jail –they literally *only* partied together. Besides that, twenty-one years old was pretty young. I was worried that her age would make her irresponsible when it came to bills and shit like that. Even the fact that she had six bands readily available to move in with a stranger was a little weird to me. With all of that being said, I was still willing to try my luck so that I didn't have to pay four bands a month for rent on my own, so I sent her pictures of the apartment and she loved it.

To actually lock things in, I confirmed with her over text that she understood that her deposit and first month's rent would be due when she moved in and that all bill money would be required on time each month after that.

THE DAY finally came for Jasmine to move in and it was a smooth transition. She basically had all new bedroom furniture delivered and all of her personal belongings were stuffed in her car and packed in suitcases or trash bags. I'm not really sure what I expected but somehow I was still very nervous about allowing that young ass girl to move into my apartment with me. Obviously I didn't show her that I was feeling that way, but something about it was just too good to be true. Anyway, once she had everything moved in she seemed super happy to just have something of her own. I mean, I didn't know her life story or anything, but I knew what it was like to move into my first apartment where I was sleeping in a bedroom that I paid for rather than my mama's house. It was a feeling of accomplishment and liberation – feelings that I kept inside when I first experienced them but Jasmine didn't keep hers inside. Seeing her feel what I believed to be the same thing I felt almost made me feel good about letting her move in with me.

The first couple of weeks were pretty normal. During the day, she was quiet. I don't know what type of shit she was doing on that webcam but I hardly ever knew she was home because she never really came out of her room. At night, I would hear her leave the house and then come back a few hours later – that was pretty much it. That all changed after about a month. Maybe she got comfortable, or maybe something in her life changed but she started coming out of her room more often and that was when I learned she was a nasty bitch. It was little things at first, like leaving a dish or two in the sink or missing the trash can when she would throw paper towels away in the bathroom. It was never a big deal at first, it was just something I wasn't used to. Destinee always cleaned up after herself and so did any other roommate I had ever had so I was trying my best to let shit go. That didn't last long because she went from being casually nasty to repulsively disgusting.

One day the bitch cooked something and I guess decided that she didn't want to eat it and left the whole fucking meal in the pots and pans on the stove for a whole fucking week! Bitch, I was pissed. The first couple of days I didn't say anything because I figured she was just busy and forgot about her whole buffet dinner that she cooked. Then, I saw her in the kitchen a couple of times. Mind you, she left more dishes in the sink, and that was when I realized she wasn't going to clean up after herself. For whatever reason I wanted to see just how long her nasty ass was going to allow the dishes and the pots and pans full of food to sit there. It sat so long that maggots started to pop up.

"Jas!" I said as I knocked on her bedroom door like I was the fucking police.

She opened the door. "Hey, girl." She smiled, like shit was sweet.

"Uhm…I'm sure you're busy but those pots and pans you left on the stove last week have maggots in them now so you gotta clean that stuff out. We can't live like that. That's disgusting." I said with a straight face.

"Oh my gosh! I completely forgot about that! My bad. I'll clean it right now." She headed toward the kitchen.

Shit, after a week on the stove and a few maggots, I didn't want those pots and pans in my house at all. She damn near could have gone in the trash with them for all I cared. She cleaned the entire kitchen though, so I let it go and chalked it up to a genuine mistake. A nasty mistake – but a mistake.

As another month passed, Jasmine started having different men over almost every single day. Not to mention, she was home all day, every day and that in itself was irritating for me because I worked from home too and it felt like I always had to see her. It was annoying because even though she was doing better about cleaning up after herself in the kitchen, her disgusting habits were still very much present in the bathroom that we shared. She would wrap her used tampons in toilet paper, throw them in the trash can and leave them there for way too many days. The bathroom would smell like old pussy because of it and it literally made me want to wring her throat. There were even times when she got out the shower dripping period blood on the floor without cleaning it up. Between that, seeing her all the fucking time and her bringing a different nigga over almost every day, I was muthafuckin' tired.

"Hey, just curious, what you got going on with work? You ever think of doing something out the house too?" I asked, trying to figure out why this bitch didn't mind living like a pig cooped up in her room all day.

She laughed, "You know what, I just got a square job, so pretty soon I'm actually going to be leaving during the day so that I can go to work."

Hearing her say that she got a 'square job' was an immediate red flag for me. See, the only time bitches call a job a 'square job' is if they're outside selling pussy. Otherwise, a job is a job – there's no such thing as a square job unless you are a prostitute. The word "square" is pimp and hoe lingo, and I knew all about that. At that point, I needed to know more because I was starting to think that the reason she was able to afford living with me was because of all of the niggas she had coming through the house everyday.

Naturally, I started trying to finesse her for the tea so I made conversation with her as if I was actually interested in her life so that she felt comfortable enough to tell me the truth. You know you have to give a little info if you want info – so I told her about the days that I was a stripper because that was no secret but I knew it would be enough for her to start running her mouth. And it was. Turns out, she had been doing the webcam shit for three years and her nigga was in jail for pimping – go fucking figure. She also explained that she had 'friends' that would give her money just to spend time with them. So long story short, she was a hoe.

After we had that little kumbaya session, Jasmine would share all her little hoe tales with me. Sometimes I would give her advice, but other times I'd just listen and remind her to keep herself safe no matter what. In some ways, I think Jas admired me as like a big sister she never had. She would always tell me that she loved the fact that I got out the strip club and bossed up or how she wanted to be like me when she was older. In some ways I was flattered in other ways I wished I hadn't allowed her to get close to me because it was too much pressure.

The idea that Jasmine looked up to me being too much pressure changed real quick the morning I woke up to the sound of her screaming. It was like the crack of dawn and I had been out partying the night before. At first, I thought I was just so drunk that my ears were ringing but when Orien kept meowing, I snapped out of it and realized what was happening. Jasmine was screaming at the top of her lungs as the sound of a male voice kept saying *shut up, bitch*. I listened for about a second when I heard a loud bang that sounded like somebody's head literally went through a wall. Right after that, Jasmine was crying even louder and I was hearing glass being broken.

"Please! Stop! Please!" I heard Jasmine cry.

That was when I knew that she was in her room getting her ass beat. As soon as I heard that glass break, I jumped out of bed and ran to her bedroom door. I started banging on her door as hard as I could, hoping that it would scare whoever the fuck was in there enough to stop putting his hands on her, but it didn't. Jas kept crying and from what I could hear, shit was still being thrown around the room.

"What the fuck are you doing?" I yelled after I kicked her bedroom door open.

The man, a tall white boy with a tattoo on his neck, back-handed Jasmine before looking at me.

"Get the fuck out of my house!" I yelled at him.

For some reason, I wasn't afraid of him. I didn't think for one second that he would put his hands on me. My only concern was making sure that he left Jasmine alone and he did. He didn't say one word to me. As he rushed past me, he bumped my shoulder with his body – I guess that was supposed to scare me. I waited a few seconds to make sure that I heard the front door close and then I ran to lock it so that he couldn't get back inside.

Jasmine was sitting in the middle of her room crying when I got back to her. She kept apologizing for what happened and swearing that it would never happen again. She ended up telling me that the nigga was her pimp-boyfriend and he was upset with her for getting a 'square job'.

"I'm trying to turn my life around, man. I just want to get out of this shit. I moved all the way to LA, got me a square ass job and just been stacking so that I can change my life around and now he's mad." She cried.

Listen, the fact that she wanted to change her life was admirable, but sis wasn't about to bring unnecessary bullshit to my house because of it. I had no sympathy for that shit.

"I feel you. Listen, I'm glad you're safe. I love that you want to turn your life around and all that. I think that's great. But that man cannot come here anymore. I do not play that domestic violence shit at all. So if you feel like you can't leave that nigga alone, you're going to have to do that somewhere else. Not here." I was extremely calm.

Jasmine wiped her tears. "No, I'm done. I swear I am. I don't owe him shit and I don't need shit from him. That was the last time. I swear." She promised.

As she was talking, I walked to the bathroom to get her a wet rag so that she could clean herself up. I didn't really have too much else to say because as long as she didn't bring that man back to my house and as long as she kept paying her bills on time, I didn't give a fuck what she did with her life. I did my part by stepping in but I wasn't going to beg her to leave no nigga alone.

I needed some time to myself after that rude awakening

and I felt like Jasmine needed some time to herself too, so I left the house and spent the day pampering myself. I went to the spa, had a rooftop lunch and then watched a movie before I was ready to go home and chill. Normally, when I get home, Orien is in my room sitting in my window sunbathing like the rich cat that he is, but he wasn't there that day. Initially, I didn't think much of it because he really just does his own thing most of the time. I took a shower and figured he'd be somewhere waiting for me when I got out, but he wasn't – which was when it started to get weird.

Y'all know Orien is practically my son, so once I got out of the shower, put some sweats on and realized I didn't see him anywhere, I started to get a little worried. I called his name a few times and looked in the places he normally hides in my room and he was nowhere to be found. When I left the house that morning, I left my bedroom door open because I was just trying to get the fuck out of there but Orien didn't usually leave my room if I wasn't home. Just to be sure, I started checking the places he'd normally hide in the living room, too. When I wasn't able to find him anywhere, I started to panic. I asked Jasmine if she had seen him and she was hella nonchalant when she told me she hadn't. It wasn't like I didn't believe her, I was just annoyed that she didn't seem to care that he was missing. At that point, I started walking around our neighborhood calling his name. I was a fucking wreck. I was crying my eyes out while I called the animal shelter to see if maybe someone had turned him in. Of course, they didn't have him either.

After like a full hour of searching high and fucking low for my son, I went back home and started checking places I would have never even considered checking because a bitch was getting desperate. I even stuck my head out of a window I had cracked open hoping he hadn't gotten out and splattered to the ground below. The very last place I checked was the laundry closet. I don't even know what made me look there but I did and low and behold – that's where he was trapped inside of the glass dryer looking like he lived in a fish tank. My heart literally skipped a beat when I opened the dryer door and he practically jumped into my arms. Tears rushed down my cheeks while I gave him hugs and kisses and apologized to him a million times for not finding him sooner. I mean, why would my cat be in the fucking dryer in the first place?!

"Jasmine!!" I yelled.

She came rushing into the hallway where the washer and dryer were.

"Why the fuck is my cat locked in the dryer?!" I was hot.

"Damn. Honestly, I don't know how he got there. I did laundry today so maybe he hopped in when I wasn't looking and then I closed him in there. My bad." She said casually.

I was so mad that I didn't say a word. I knew that she had a rough start to her day seeing as though she woke up to getting her ass beat by a nigga but like damn, how do you not see my cat in the fucking dryer, bro? I was irritated the entire rest of the day. Between the domestic violence that happened that morning and locking my cat in the dryer that afternoon, Jasmine was on her second strike in my mind. Paying all of the bills on my own didn't sound like the worst idea at that point. I mean obviously I wasn't going to make any permanent decisions based on my temporary emotions but that was a lot for me in one day. Not to mention she was still leaving used tampons in the trash can for too long and had my bathroom smelling like rotten coochie if I didn't force her to take out her trash. It was just too much for me and the only way to prevent myself from going off on her was for me to stay in my room for the rest of the night – which was exactly what I did.

———

THE NEXT COUPLE of weeks were a little calmer. Jasmine wasn't home as much because she was waking up every morning to go to her 'square job'. I don't know if she kept fucking with her "boyfriend" after he beat her ass but she wasn't bringing him to the house so I minded my business. In order for me to keep my sanity I would work from home during the day while she wasn't there and book studio sessions at night so that I didn't have to deal with her when she got home. It was a win-win for me which was cool because it kept me focused on what mattered – accomplishing my dreams and getting my money. Every now and then I would entertain whatever man was in my DM's trying to link with me but I would always find an excuse when it was time to actually link. Ya girl had had enough heartbreak to last a lifetime so I was trying to stay away from niggas for as long as I could.

One night, I was getting in super late from the studio and the closer I got to my apartment door, the louder the sounds of a cat meowing became. Now, it was around Halloween and my neighbors all had decorations up in their windows and on their doors so I was thinking that someone's decorations included a cat somehow. You know, like a witch and a black cat or some shit. My happy ass is stopping at damn near every decorated door to check out the decorations and see which door had the cat sounds but by the time I got further down the hallway, I hadn't seen one single cat. As soon as I hit the corner guess what the fuck I see. Orien. My damn son was standing in front of my apartment door crying at the top of his lungs, waiting to be let inside. You know I was pissed!

The first thing I did was pick him up and make sure that

he wasn't hurt and when I saw that he was perfectly fine, I rushed inside the house.

"Jasmine! Why the fuck is my cat outside?!" I yelled without even knowing if she was home or where she was in the house.

I slammed the door behind me and realized that the entire house was pitch black and for whatever reason, that pissed me off even more. I walked to my bedroom with Orien in my arms and gently placed him onto my bed and put my purse down next to him. My plan was to bang on Jasmine's bedroom door until she woke up because at that point, she had me fucked up. Her bedroom door was open just a little which meant that she wasn't home because she always left her bedroom door cracked a little whenever she left.

It was probably a good thing that she wasn't home though because ain't no tellin' what she would have said when I asked her why Orien was outside and there was really no tellin' what I would have done if I didn't like her answer. I hated that she wasn't home for me to cuss her out but I was happy that Orien was safe and inside. That was my final straw though. Strike three, bitch. It was nice having a roommate that paid her bills on time but I knew that allowing Jasmine's young ass to live with me was a risk. Shit, it was actually a liability at that point and it was one I definitely couldn't afford. That night, I made the decision that Jasmine had to get the fuck out my house. I spent the entire night looking for cheaper apartments.

The next morning, I could hear Jasmine turn the shower water off, so I knew that she was home and I didn't even care to wait until she got dressed before I said what I needed to say.

"Hey." I said as she walked from the bathroom to her bedroom. "I just realized that our lease is ending at the end of this month, so we're going to have to move out. I mean, you're welcome to like apply here and find a new roommate if you want but otherwise, we have to be out of here by the 1st." I said as I leaned against my bedroom door and folded my arms across my chest.

That was a bold-faced lie but I didn't give two fucks. I don't know if the bitch intentionally put Orien in the dryer or left him outside but it didn't matter. It didn't matter because I wasn't about to give her another opportunity to show me if it was on purpose or not and asking her why he was outside the night before wasn't going to change the fact that my poor baby was out there – for who knows how long. Jasmine was just lucky that I had calmed down from the night before.

Jasmine stopped in her tracks and made sure that her towel was secured around her body. "Damn. That's like two weeks from now. Is there an option for us to just renew this lease together?" She asked.

In my head I was like *bitch, don't nobody want to live with your nasty ass*!

"No, I'm actually just going to get a one-bedroom downtown. It's closer to the studio I record at and I'm thinking about opening up a storefront down there. So, it just makes more sense for me to downsize all together." I lied.

"Oh, that's dope. Ok. Well, I guess we're out of here in two weeks then." She said.

I didn't even bother replying because I was so annoyed. Plus, I had already found and applied for a new apartment and was just waiting to hear back from the leasing office, so I didn't care what Jasmine was about to do or where she was about to go as long as she got the fuck up out my face.

OUTSIDE OF THE domestic violence thing, I didn't care about how Jasmine got her money. She was a young bitch getting to the bag the best way she knew how and I can't ever knock a bitch for that. She got a little better at cleaning up after herself in the kitchen but she was still disgusting in the bathroom and that, on top of her carelessness with Orien, whether it was accidental or deliberate was way too much for me. Anyway, over the next two weeks, we packed up the apartment and prepared to go our separate ways. Jasmine had a lot of growing and learning to do and I had my own shit to deal with so I wasn't in a position to be patient enough to be her teacher.

Jasmine ended up leaving the apartment without saying anything on moving day. When I checked her room to make sure it was cleared out I was disgusted to find the white carpet was black from the amount of different niggas she had walking all through that shit. Not to mention her leaving her entire bed frame and trash all throughout the room. It was a good thing she left without saying anything because that on top of everything else would have been a one way ticket to getting her ass beat by me.

Besides having to hire cleaners for Jasmine's room, moving out was smooth for me. I hired movers and they were in and out of the old apartment in like an hour tops. I signed my new lease while the movers unloaded the truck and placed all of my stuff into my new home. It didn't really hit me that I was moving into an apartment on my own until I walked in and realized every box and piece of furniture was mine and no one else's. It was really crazy to think that after all of the living situations I had been in throughout my life, none of them were me moving into a place on my own with no intentions of having a roommate or friend living with me. It was bittersweet but I was ready. So ready that I actually started unpacking everything right then and there.

It only took me about three days to fully unpack, decorate and set up my new apartment. For those three days, I didn't really have time to think about anything other than unpacking. I'm not sure if that was intentional or if I was just super focused on getting it done but when that three days was up and I woke up on that fourth day, in my fully furnished apartment with no one but Orien and myself, everything came crashing down on me. It was a very hot and cold moment for me because on one hand, I was happy to be living alone but on the other hand, I felt lonely. It's funny because I had so many friends, thousands of followers across all of my social media platforms and some of the richest, most famous men sending me messages trying to date me but somehow I still felt alone.

Waking up on that fourth day was probably the most reflective moment I had in my entire life. It was the moment that I realized that I needed more than just a change in scenery to help me through all of the traumatic events I had experienced in my life. It was the moment that I realized that I needed therapy. There wasn't anything normal about my childhood and nothing healthy about a majority of my life as an adult. I realized that I had never really healed from one thing before the next thing happened and I was always just doing whatever I needed to in order to survive. Don't get me wrong, I think it's necessary to do what you have to do to get by – I'm sure I've said that to you before, but I had finally realized that you're never really living if you're always fighting to survive.

See, I allowed myself to get caught up in what other people thought of me. I mean, it was pretty hard not to. If you think about it, dating all the way back to the days where people knew of me because of my tattoos and then because I was a stripper and then because of who I was dating or the show I was on – I've always been under some sort of spotlight where I felt like what people thought of me actually mattered. There's been so many moments in my life where I refused to get help because I didn't want people to know the pain I was experiencing – or that I even had hardships. Not to mention times where I've kept my mouth shut about my abuse because having a victim mentality on an internet full of people who want to see you fail never seemed smart. It dawned on me that none of that was really healthy.

The trauma that I've experienced in my private life forced me to feel like I needed to hide the real me in the public eye. I felt like in order to succeed and be liked, I had to hide the fact that I felt pain, experienced trauma, had family drama, had my heart broken by men, struggled financially or just didn't have it all together all the time. As I laid in my bed that morning, I realized that I felt as though I had to hide the pieces of myself that made me who I was. I realized that the same pieces I was hiding were the same pieces everyone else was hiding too. Being alone in my apartment helped me realize that there was no amount of money or fame that mattered if I wasn't going to be true to myself.

That morning, I made a pact with myself that from that day forward, I wouldn't care what people thought of me and I wouldn't hide the fact that I go through shit just like everybody else. I decided that from that day forward, I would leave a man at the first sign of toxicity and I wouldn't pour more into someone else than they poured into me. I decided that I was going to start going to therapy because even though people thought that I had all my shit together based on what they saw, the truth was that all that glitters ain't gold.. That morning, I decided that I was ready to heal.

CONNECTING

WINTERBLANCOMUSIC@GMAIL.COM

ALSO BY KAILA WILKEY

See, I Was Right

Made in United States
North Haven, CT
15 February 2024

48793531R10134